BOOK 7

WATERING
AND
FEEDING

THE MANUAL OF
STABLE MANAGEMENT

The Kenilworth Press I

THE ADVISORY PANEL INCLUDED

Barbara Slane-Fleming FBHS
Tessa Martin-Bird FBHS
Stewart Hastie MRCVS
Jeremy Houghton-Brown B Phil Ed
Helen Webber FBHS
Gillian McCarthy BSc
Elizabeth Launder MSc
Deborah Lucas MSc
Pat Smallwood FBHS
Judy Cammaerts FBHS

SERIES EDITOR
Jane Kidd

British Library Cataloguing in Publication Data
A catalogue record for this book is available from the British Library

ISBN 0-901366-68-4

Produced for the British Horse Society by
The Kenilworth Press Ltd
Addington, Buckingham, MK18 2JR

Typeset in 11/13 Candida by Bookworm Typesetting
Printed and bound in Great Britain by
Hollen Street Press Ltd, Berwick upon Tweed

CONTENTS

Introduction   5

The Horse's Natural Way of Life   7

Part 1 – Watering

1	The Necessity of Water	11
2	The Principles of Watering	13
3	Systems of Watering for Stabled Horses	15
4	Watering Competition Horses	17
5	Dehydration	19

Part 2 – Feeding

6	Food and Digestion	25
7	The Rules of Feeding	38
8	Composition of Food	42
9	Types of Food	51
10	Deciding on a Ration	69
11	Rations for Different Types of Horse	82
12	Feeding Problems and Non-Routine Feeding	96
13	Preparing Food	103
14	The Feed Shed and Storing Food	110

Appendices

Appendix 1 – Rationing   117
Appendix 2 – Metrication   121
Appendix 3 – Useful Tables   123
   Table 1 – Ratio of Hay to Concentrates During
     Fittening Work   123
   Table 2 – Percentages of Body Weight as Total
     Dry Food Requirement   124
   Table 3 – Nutritive Value of Some Common
     Foods   125
Bibliography   126
Glossary   127
Index   137

Introduction

The aim of this series is to provide a reliable source of information and advice on all practical aspects of horse and stable management. Throughout the series emphasis is placed on the adoption of correct and safe procedures for the welfare of all who come into contact with horses, as well as for the animals themselves.

The books have been compiled by a panel of experts, each drawing on considerable experience and contributing specialised knowledge on his or her chosen subject.

The other titles in the series are:

Book 1, The Horse – Conformation; Action; Psychology of the Horse; Teeth and Ageing; Breeds; Breeding; Identification; Buying and Selling; Glossary of Terms.

Book 2, Care of the Horse – Handling the Horse; Stable Vices and Problem Behaviour; Grooming; Bedding; Clipping, Trimming, Pulling and Plaiting; Recognising Good Health and Caring for the Sick Horse; Internal Parasites; Shoeing.

Book 3, The Horse at Grass – Grassland Management; Management of Horses and Ponies at Grass; Working the Grass-kept Pony or Horse; Bringing a Horse up from Grass.

Book 4, Saddlery – Saddles; Bridles; Other Saddlery; Bits; Boots and Bandages; Clothing; Care and Cleaning of Leather; Saddling and Unsaddling.

Book 5, Specialist Care of the Competition Horse – Dressage Horse; Driving Horse; Show Jumper; Event Horse; Long-Distance Horse; Hunter; Show Horse or Pony; Point-to-Pointer; Polo Pony; Types of Transportation; Travelling.

Book 6, The Stable Yard – Construction; Riding Schools; Organising and Running a Yard; The Buying of Fodder and Bedding; The Law.

Book 7, Watering and Feeding – Watering; Natural Feeding; The Digestive System; Principles of Feeding; Foodstuffs; Rations; Problem Eaters; The Feed Shed, Storage and Bulk Purchasing.

NOTE: *Throughout the book the term 'horses' is used and it will often include ponies.*

The Horse's Natural Way of Life

Before horses were domesticated they lived in herds ranging over a wide area. They ate herbage, grasses and bushes, all high in fibre and soluble nutrients. The wide choice of plants provided the necessary nutrients. Creatures of flight rather than fight, they drank only once or twice daily because the food they were eating contained a high percentage of water. This natural way of life can still be observed in the zebra herds living in Africa.

Horses were, and still are, what is known as trickle feeders, eating almost continually throughout a twenty-four hour period. Our domesticated horses and ponies living out at grass have kept the same instincts and habits but within the limitations of fencing and hedges.

However, our modern horses could not survive the same conditions as their ancestors. They have, through selective breeding, become much bigger and more fragile creatures.

The horsemaster should remember the natural habits of the horse and try to reproduce the same conditions as far as possible. He should try to arrange his feeding programme so that it is spread out over as long a time as possible and does not include long periods where no food is available. He must make sure, too, that there is sufficient fibre in the rations.

Horses living out will do much better on a large area of natural grazing than on a small area of rich, improved grass. However, moorland ponies, although their native haunts provide a large area in which to graze, do have health problems in today's world. Modern man alters their habitat, interferes with their numbers and prevents them from reaching the good and most suitable grazing. They often suffer severe worm infestation, due to high-density stocking and lack of cross-grazing with other animals. Somewhat similar problems can exist in horses living on fenced grazing.

PART 1

Watering

CHAPTER 1
The Necessity of Water

Water is essential for life and health. Horses can stay alive without food for a few weeks but without water they would probably die after five to six days.

Water makes up approximately 65% of an adult horse's body weight and almost 80% of a foal's body weight. Every cellular activity requires water. It is present in all body fluids, which are in three compartments: blood, intercellular fluid and intracellular fluid.

Water is essential for:

DIGESTION   —   as saliva, which helps swallowing; water also provides a fluid medium for the food to pass along the digestive tract and provides the basis for digestive juices.

BLOOD   —   the fluid containing blood cells and nutrients etc. which circulates round the body and also carries waste from the tissues.

LYMPH   —   to drain tissue and help maintain the right balance of body fluid. It is important for defence against disease.

URINE   —   to excrete the waste products, and as a vehicle to regulate levels of sodium, potassium and other electrolytes as determined by kidney function.

FAECES   —   to supply fluid to aid excretion.

BODY   —   to regulate the body temperature by transferring excess heat to the surface.

SKIN   —   to get rid of surplus heat as sweat.

EYES AND NOSTRILS	—	in the form of tears and mucus as a lubricant.
JOINTS	—	in the form of 'oil' as a lubricant.
MILK	—	to make 91% of the milk of lactating mares.

Daily Requirements

In their natural state horses are trickle feeders grazing more or less continually. In doing so they take in a considerable amount of water as all growing plants contain a large percentage of water. Horses in the wild normally do not drink more than once or twice daily, at dawn and sunset, unless the herbage is particularly dry or the weather very hot.

Stabled horses eat conserved food, with a water content averaging about 14%. It is therefore necessary to have water always available so that they can make up this deficiency. Some horses will drink between eating mouthfuls of their concentrate food. Most will drink after eating concentrates and roughage, especially the latter.

A stabled horse on dry food requires 20–40 litres (5–10 gallons) of water a day depending on the work he is doing and the weather. A lactating mare with a foal at foot requires considerably more.

An 8% deficiency of water, however lost from the horse's body, causes sub-acute illness. A loss of 15% causes dehydration and possibly death, especially if associated with heat exhaustion.

CHAPTER 2
The Principles of Watering

Horses should have clean fresh water available at all times. If this is not possible, for example after exercise or when travelling, they should be offered some water before they are fed.

Horses that have free and constant access to water rarely drink very much at one time.

Care should be taken that horses do not drink excessively before fast work. For racing, when maximum effort is required for only a short time, water may be removed before a race but never for longer than 4 hours. The watering of competition horses is covered on page 17.

Purity of Water
Horses are extremely fussy about water. If it is tainted in any way they will go thirsty rather than drink it. Even a change of water may cause rejection. Water that has stood for any length of time in plastic containers may be rejected. Sometimes the addition of a little glucose or molasses will persuade horses to drink. 'Hard' water is probably preferable to 'soft' water but the important point is that it is clean and fresh.

Any suspicion of dung in buckets or water bowls will prevent a horse drinking.

It is sometimes recommended that medicines are put in the drinking water. This can be unwise as the horse will usually refuse to drink what he considers to be contaminated water.

Water may be contaminated by various substances, including lead, which can be dissolved from lead pipes by acid water. All piping should therefore be lead-free.

The main storage tank for the stable yard should be checked

regularly. A dust and vermin proof cover should be used.

If horses are seen to play and fuss with their water this is likely to be due to contamination, but could be a sign of a sub-acute colic attack.

CHAPTER 3
Systems of Watering for Stabled Horses
(See also Book 6)

Automatic Water Bowls

Advantages

- Water always available.
- Labour-saving.

Disadvantages

- Can cause physical injury unless boxed in.
- Liable to destruction from horse activity.
- Unable to monitor amount of water being drunk.
- Not suitable for mares and foals.
- Difficult to clean.

Water bowls must be large enough for the horse to get his muzzle in with ease. They should be of the self-filling kind with a small ball-cock, and preferably with a plug to facilitate emptying and cleaning. The inlet pipe must be well insulated to prevent freezing and should have a stopcock.

Gravity-filling bowls are sometimes installed but can prove troublesome. Also, bowls which have a plate for the animal to press with its nose are not suitable for horses.

Water bowls must be emptied and cleaned frequently. In big yards they must be inspected daily by a single competent person.

Buckets

Advantages

- Water consumption can be monitored.

Disadvantages

- Labour-intensive.
- Can be knocked over.
- Horse may be without water at times.

Buckets should be large (14 litre/3 gallon for preference) and of heavy-duty material. They are usually made of PVC.

Buckets should be emptied and refilled twice daily. They should be topped up at midday, or more often. Cleaning should be done with plain water and a brush kept specially for the purpose. If light colours are chosen for the buckets it will be easier to see if they have been properly cleaned.

Buckets should be put in a corner of the box with the handle turned away from the horse. They should be well banked up with bedding to prevent them from being knocked over. They should not be put by the door but preferably near the drainage outlet.

Buckets with handles are not suitable for foals (see also *Book 6, The Stable Yard*).

NOTE: For watering in the field see *Book 3, The Horse at Grass*.

CHAPTER 4
Watering Competition Horses

Event Horses
Providing the horses have had free access to water they will not need a long drink before the competition starts. This will particularly apply at a three-day event where the horses are stabled nearby, but at a one-day event, if the horses have travelled some distance, they should be offered water immediately on arrival. Half a bucket of water drunk 20 minutes before starting work will do no harm because the dressage phase requires no fast, strenuous exertion. Event horses should be allowed a small amount of water between each phase to maintain their body fluids. More may be given if the gaps between phases are very long.

At a three-day event most veterinary surgeons now consider that horses should be offered a few mouthfuls of water – 1 litre (2 pints) – in the box before the cross-country. If it is possible to arrange, a few mouthfuls should be given at the end of phase B, the steeplechase. This is especially important in warm, humid conditions.

After the cross-country is completed, and as soon as the horse's breathing is back to normal and he shows no signs of distress, he may be given 2¼ litres (½ gallon) of water every 15 minutes until he is satisfied. Electrolytes may be given, but plain water should also be offered. It is important that the horse drinks and if he appears distressed, veterinary advice should be sought immediately. (See 'Signs of Dehydration', page 19.)

Long-Distance Riding Horses

Much veterinary research has been done on long-distance riding horses. It has been found that the best method of avoiding dehydration is to allow the horses *ad lib* water whenever possible during the ride. If this has been done the horse should be allowed 2¼ litres (½ gallon) every 5 minutes after finishing the ride. If water has not been available on the ride 2¼ litres (½ gallon) every 15 minutes may be allowed. Electrolytes may be added but the horse *must* drink, so plain water should also be available.

Hunters

Hunters should be allowed unrestricted access to water before hunting.

If the journey home in the box or trailer is longer than 30 minutes, the horses should be offered water before they start travelling. On arrival home, if they are cool and dry and do not appear distressed they should be allowed water *ad lib*.

If they are hot they should be allowed 2¼ litres (½ gallon) of water every 15 minutes. If they are distressed, veterinary help should be sought. (See 'Dehydration', opposite.)

CHAPTER 5
Dehydration

Dehydration results when more water and salts are lost from the body than are taken in and the horse has not enough fluid in his body to maintain normal physiological conditions. It is usually associated with fast, energetic work but there are many other situations in which dehydration can occur.

Possible Causes of Dehydration

- Lack of available water or failure to drink.
- Sweating – prolonged and marked.
- Diarrhoea – especially in foals.
- Excessive urination when not accompanied by a compensatory thirst.
- Haemorrhage.
- Heat exhaustion.

Dehydration may result in:

- Reduced performance.
- Muscle damage.
- Colic.
- Reduced kidney function.
- Laminitis.
- Azoturia (rhabdomyolysis).
- Coma.
- Death.

Signs of Dehydration

- Skin loses its pliability (see 'Pinch Test', below).
- Lack of inclination to graze or eat.

Dehydration

- Listlessness.
- Loss of normal colour from the membranes of gums and eyes and reduced membrane refill time.
- Muscles quiver.
- Pulse becomes small.
- 'Thumps' (see below).
- Thick, patchy sweat.
- Panting (only if in association with heat exhaustion).

Any horse showing the above symptoms after severe exertion should have veterinary attention immediately. Dehydration can be confirmed by blood-testing.

Pinch test
A fold of skin on the neck is picked up between finger and thumb. If when released it does not return to normal in 5 seconds, the horse is dehydrated to some extent.

'Thumps' (synchronous diaphragmatic flutter)
The diaphragm contracts in the same rhythm as the heart beat so the horse's flanks synchronise with the pulse. The contractions may even be heard. Veterinary advice should be sought immediately.

CAUSES OF DEHYDRATION

Lack of Water

This may be a chronic, on-going, low-grade dehydration where animals are not provided with a *sufficient* supply of *fresh, clean* water over a long period of time. Poor performance will follow and is one cause of the horse's fitness being 'over the top'.

It is likely to occur in the following situations:

- ☐ Ponies at grass, particularly those on tethers, who are watered from a bucket or other inadequate supply.
- ☐ Stabled horses who are only offered water at stated times.
- ☐ Stabled horses whose water bowls are not cleaned regularly.
- ☐ Stabled horses whose buckets are not cleaned, emptied and refilled regularly and thereafter kept full. The available

water may be tainted.
☐ Water being withheld deliberately.

It is not unknown for dealers, and riders especially in dressage, show jumping and showing to withhold water so that the horse becomes partially dehydrated and therefore quieter. This is iniquitous and can result in permanent damage to the horse. If this happens in a three-day event, even if the horse is given water *ad lib* after the dressage, he will start the cross-country below par.

Sweating

Man and horse are the only animals that regulate their temperature by sweating.

When the horse sweats, he will lose valuable electrolytes; the most important being sodium, chloride and potassium.

Excess sweating is usually caused by long-term strenuous work such as long-distance riding. It is the duration of sweating which is important but temperature *and* humidity are important factors.

Other causes of sweating include:

- Travelling.
- Illness, especially obstructive colics.
- Stress.
- Fear.
- Pain.
- Excitement.
- Airless hot stable with high humidity prevents evaporation and may lead to heat stress.

If these cause dehydration, water and electrolytes (essential salts) are necessary for recovery. In severe case veterinary assistance is indicated.

Travelling

(See also *Book 5, Specialist Care of the Competition Horse*)
Travelling, even short distances, can be a stressful experience for the horse. Some horses, however accustomed they are to travelling, will refuse to eat while in the vehicle and will not drink even when stationary. These horses must be treated with

21

great care as there is a danger of dehydration and colic is more likely when they start eating at the end of the journey.

During any breaks in travelling, watering is a top priority and, if possible, some grazing.

Horses can also suffer dehydration due to excessive sweating on the journey. This is particularly likely with young horses unaccustomed to travelling. It is not always appreciated how much they have sweated as the air blowing through the vehicle may dry them off and 'hide' the extent of the sweating.

Diarrhoea

Diarrhoea will cause dehydration. It is especially serious in the case of foals. Acute diarrhoea will require replacement therapy urgently. Horses that are ill or are suffering from the effects of worm infestation causing chronic diarrhoea should have electrolyte salts added to their diets in addition to the anthelmintic treatment given under veterinary supervision.

Excessive Urination

This may be the result of overprolonged dosing with a diuretic. Veterinary advice should be sought. However, the horse with polyuria (excessive urination) will usually develop a compensatory polydypsia (increased thirst).

ELECTROLYTES – see Glossary

These are a mixture of minerals which are added to the water or feed after strenuous exercise. It is pointless giving them a long time before a competition, but to get horses used to the taste they may be offered. daily after work for a week or so. With a commercial preparation it is important to check that the proportions are correct. If glucose is incorporated, it is there to increase absorption and not as a source of energy. Veterinary advice regarding electrolyte supplementation is worthwhile.

If electrolytes are given after a competition, plain water should also be offered. It is *extremely* important to get the horse to drink. In cases of extreme exhaustion the veterinary surgeon may give the horse fluid intravenously as in this case oral rehydration can be dangerous.

PART · 2

Feeding

CHAPTER 6

Food and Digestion

THE NECESSITY OF FOOD

Food is needed by the horse for:

- Maintenance of life.
- Growth and/or work.
- Repair of tissues.

It is the source of energy.

Energy is needed for all the body processes, such as the nerves, the heart, the digestion, the lungs, the control of body temperature, the muscles, both voluntary and involuntary, and especially for muscular activity.

DIGESTION

This book is primarily concerned with the nutrition of the horse: the feedstuffs, the diet, the rationing and the feeding principles. A detailed description of the anatomy and the physiology of the digestive system and the related structures and functionings will be found in the companion volume, *The BHS Veterinary Manual*, and in those sources listed therein under 'References' and 'Suggested Reading'.

It should be appreciated that learning about the anatomy and the physiology of any of the body systems just for the sake of more advanced theoretical knowledge is not a substitute for sound, practical skills gained under an experienced and trained teacher and based on *essential* theoretical knowledge.

Food and Digestion

In this chapter the emphasis is on those particular features of the system which are practically related to a better understanding of the rules which govern the art and the science of feeding. Knowledge of these features can be considered a basic requirement of responsible horsemanship at any level. Such responsibility is directed towards the skills concerned with feeding, which is one aspect of the welfare of the horse.

The aims of feeding are to:

- Maintain health.
- Maximise performance.
- Minimise nutritional mistakes.
- Reduce the risks of malnutrition in all its aspects.

The more advanced the athletic performance of the horse, the greater the attention needed to detailed application of the skills. Although background knowledge, as distinct from this essential knowledge, is not necessarily required, it is assumed that stable managers so involved will wish to increase their theory. The 'what', 'when', and 'how' are more efficiently put into practice if the 'why' is also understood.

Any theoretical knowledge gained should be primarily directed towards the practical ability to:

☐ Appreciate when all is well, and that the horse is at ease.
☐ To recognise quickly when all is not well, and the horse is at 'dis-ease', as judged by the clues produced by the structures and functionings of the system(s) involved.

The 'feeding of the horse is in the eye of the master'!

The art of feeding horses has been practised and taught for over 3000 years. The scientific understanding is much younger. Most of the research which has substantiated the art has been carried out during the last fifty years. It must not be forgotten, however, that the horse has not basically changed in many thousands of years. Its instincts and behaviour as a nomadic, gregarious *herbivore*, its appetite and its digestive system, have not altered since it became *Equus caballus*, an established plains dweller living by grazing and browsing.

It is still constructed and 'programmed' to survive by eating vegetation, and although the vegetation to which it has access has changed, it has done so only to a degree.

These changes first occurred as the various 'types' of horse spread out into Europe and Asia to settle in different climatically controlled areas:

- Mountain and moorland.
- Lusher lowland pastures.
- Steppes and prairies.
- Deserts.

Early domestication within these broad locations still depended upon 'natural' eating.

Farming practices in those countries where seasonal changes in grass growth occurred (temperate zones), eventually produced methods of conserving herbage for over-winter feeding, followed by the development of harvested indigenous grains. More recent centuries recognised the need for energy intakes on a daily basis in excess of what grass, hay and unimproved grain could supply, and horsemen learnt how to concentrate the ration by using progressively more improved cereal crops of denser, therefore richer, starch content so that they met the energy requirements within the limitations of the horse's daily capacity. Thus began 'unnatural' feeding practices.

Modern feeding may seem to be a complicated business of permutations of many indigenous and foreign materials but, with few exceptions, these are all vegetations and their by-products and they are basically similar to the horse's 'natural' foods but with marked differences in starch content and mineral ratios. It is these which make such rations 'unnatural'.

The Characteristics of Plants – seen from a 'horse feed' aspect.
Vegetation converts the energy of the sun on leaf chlorophyll (via photosensitisation) into plant energy for:

☐ Growth and maturation. To these ends the metabolic processes produce compounds of carbon, hydrogen, oxygen, nitrogen, etc. as carbohydrates, proteins, lipids and vitamins and, along with minerals from the soil, these are the solubles and suspensions in the fluid or sap; and a compound carbohydrate, *cellulose*, which gives shape and strength to the plant.

☐ The development of the reproductive system, the flower and ultimately the seed, both of which replicate the constituents of the parts; except that the seed requires a concentrated form of nutrient to nourish the eventual germination. This is starch, another form of carbohydrate.

All these are potential sources of energy for the grazing horse. It can be said that plants store energy and that horses expend energy (in growth, repair and work).

The most important component is *cellulose*. Under natural feeding this carbohydrate forms by far the greatest part of the horse's staple diet BUT its energy value can be released only by *microbial* fermentation within specialised areas of the digestive system: the caecum and large intestine. It cannot be digested in the ordinary 'omnivorous' way, although the other constituents can. Some of these solubles are also used to nourish the micro-organisms.

When cellulose is broken down it produces large quantities of volatile fatty acids which are absorbed into the system and metabolised into energy sources and stores. It is this microbial digestion which is inferred by the classification *herbivorous*.

The Micro-organisms
There are several species always present in the digestive tract. The relative proportions vary with the predominant pasture strains. Some are adapted for fermenting lush grass cellulose, others for the stemmier types and yet others for the husks of seeds. Yet again other strains are concerned with those un-digested solubles and starch that reach the large intestine.

The Horse and its Herbivorous Diet
Grass, even when fresh, succulent and high in water content, is still a fibre-rich plant containing comparatively small amounts of solubles. The horse must ingest large quantities: on average, approximately 2½% of his own body weight as dry matter intake. He eats for the greater part of a twenty-four hour day and

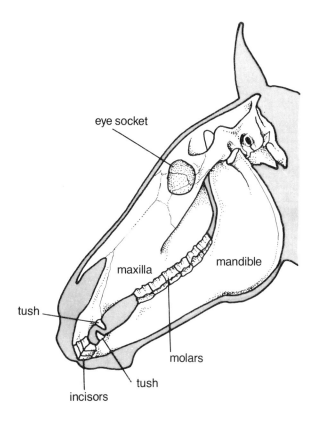

eye socket

maxilla

mandible

tush

molars

tush

incisors

Headbones and permanent teeth, (skull and lower jaw).

for long periods at a time. Such is called *trickle feeding.*

An inherited instinct is the desire not only to eat but to eat foodstuffs which have the stimulus to instigate *mastication.* The horse 'feels the need to chew' and the fibrous nature of even wet grass guarantees this satisfaction.

Mastication takes time, requires powerful jaw muscles to move the lower jaw across the upper, and long jaws to accommodate large molar teeth. These are set back in the jaws away from the incisor teeth, and the tushes if present, the spaces between being called the bars. This anterior (rostral) area allows the food, prehended by the *lips* and cut off by the *incisor teeth* to be collected by the *tongue* and propelled backwards to between

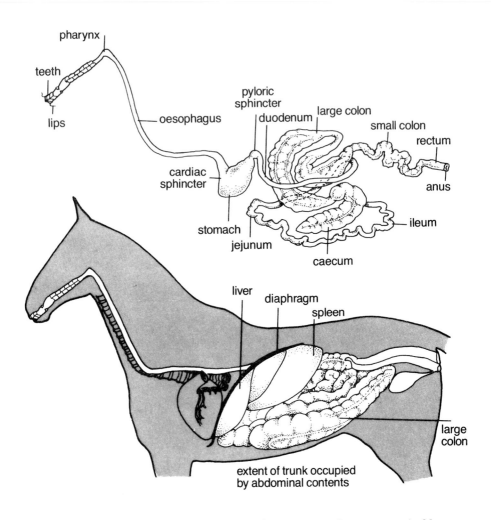

The digestive system (simplified). Note the greater volume occupied by the abdominal contents relative to heart and lungs (see also illustrations opposite) and the relative, much larger volume of large intestines (colon) and caecum compared to the stomach and small intestines (colon).

tongue and *mouth roof* and the molar arcades. (Space in the lower jaw for the bit is fortuitous!)

Characteristically the grazing (eating) horse continually eats and chews. As it does so, mastication stimulates the flow of copious *parotid saliva*. In addition to acting as a lubricant the watery saliva carries certain electrolytes and antacids. As the chewed food passes into the throat (pharynx) it is moulded into

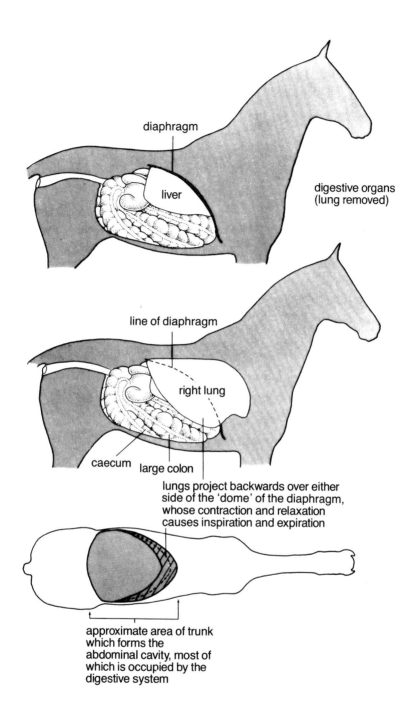

diaphragm

liver

digestive organs
(lung removed)

line of diaphragm

right lung

caecum   large colon

lungs project backwards over either
side of the 'dome' of the diaphragm,
whose contraction and relaxation
causes inspiration and expiration

approximate area of trunk
which forms the
abdominal cavity, most of
which is occupied by the
digestive system

Diagrams showing relative positions of digestive organs and lungs.

elongated boluses before entering the gullet (oesophagus) en route to the stomach wherein simple digestion begins. The cellulose particles pass through that organ and the small intestine and in no more than 6 hours enters the blind gut (caecum) and the large intestine (large, compound and small, simple colon) before the undigested material is voided after some 40 hours or so.

The stomach never quite empties but does intermittently fill according to the grazing pattern. The large intestine and caecum never empty. There is always a constant topping up and an on-going fermentation with audible gut sounds.

The stomach is relatively small and so is liable to overfill, especially when feeds are lush and suddenly available after periods of scarcity. Its construction is such that burping (eructation) and vomiting cannot occur.

Mastication serves other important functions besides stimulating saliva:

- It lacerates the stem, leaf, flower and seed.
- It liberates the sap with its solubles.

Incidentally, a horse does not salivate at the sight, smell, taste or 'sound' of foodstuffs.

Under 'natural' grazing the horse may show herbage variety preferences but all the nutrients in each and every grass, legume or plant are ingested and utilised. There is, of course, a residual undigestible component.

Changes in nutrient ratios related to growth rates of the herbage are minor or slow in onset, associated more with the seasons than with weather variables. The micro-organism colonies, once established, therefore remain fairly steady and they suffer no 'dis-ease', as can happen with sudden and dramatic feed intake changes. Consequently gut function, subsequent metabolism, and ultimate life and work remain in a 'steady state'.

Stabling, winter feeding and feeding for high performance require quite marked changes for the horse's digestive system. Grass is replaced by hay and allied products with its higher dry matter, stemmier consistency, i.e. more cellulose and less solubles, now collectively called *roughage*.

The energy input is obtained from increasing use of grains – cereal seeds – which are rich in starch, densely packed, hence the name *concentrates*.

It is any change to the dietary regime which demands good stable management.

Hay, which as a general rule should not be less than 30% and never less than 25% by weight of the total ration, is eaten slowly but it is impossible not to have periods within the 24 hours when eating and chewing is not required. Corn is eaten quickly. It should be mixed, 'opened', with chopped roughage, bran or soaked sugar beet to slow up ingestion and encourage better chewing.

The effect of mistakes in these changes are dealt with elsewhere but always:

- Offer hay after grain.
- Offer the largest amount of hay after the evening feed.
- Change from grass to hay slowly over 7–10 days.
- Establish on hay before introducing grain.
- Offer no more than 500g grain (roughly 1lb) for a 500 kg (1100 lbs) horse on day one and increase daily by no more than 200g (½ lb) daily till maximum is reached. Remember that the work which requires concentrates progresses slowly anyway.
- Never put more than 2 kg (4½ lbs) of feed in the manger at one time.
- Feeds should be divided into at least two per day and more as feed is increased.
- Make sure that there is always plenty of water.

Routine Horsemanship
Once settled on to a pasture, a horse will graze for up to 16 out of 24 hours. This will be broken up into variable sessions, more at night in warm weather but usually the longest periods in daylight. It is not known what regulates the horse's appetite.

Horses tend to walk forward as they graze. Occasionally they'll lift their head and neck to check out the environment, but continue to chew. Most will stop grazing and come to, or at least heed, a call from the owner/handler.

At the end of a grazing session various activities will follow:

- Close contact with a 'friend' for mutual grooming.
- Exercise with other horses.
- Movement to excretory areas, but horses rarely void urine and faeces at same time.
- Rest: standing, sternal recumbency or lateral recumbency.

Deviations from known behaviour should attract attention. Interpretation and assessment is described in other manuals but beware the horse that stands 'away from herd', refuses to stand up on stimulation, or shows no interest in his preferred tit-bit or plucked grass.

It is fortuitous if defaecation is observed during any visit to inspect the horse. The sudden appearance of a soiled tail and bottom in the grazing animal should be investigated.

In the stable, evidence of a horse 'off food' is seen in the manger and hay net, if feed and hay are untouched or thrown on to the floor. A badly disturbed bed and marked alteration in the number of droppings, especially if down to nil, and changes in their colour, consistency and smell are all important clues. Partially chewed, dropped out wads of hay, grass etc. indicate an acute mouth problem. Copious salivation, especially down the nostrils, with intermittent marked swallowing attempts, indicate oesophageal choke which requires urgent veterinary attention.

In the stable
It takes a horse about 40 minutes to consume 1 kg (roughly 2 lbs) hay; straight hard feeds take about 10 minutes for 1 kg (2 lbs). When openers, especially chaff, are added, this time will be doubled or trebled.

A horse will defaecate eight to twelve times in 24 hours. (During working hours there is no excuse for more than one 'pat' in the bedding at any one time.)

The horse can be seen to eat, seen and heard to masticate; and seen to swallow (the bolus passes down the left jugular groove at intervals during eating and chewing). He can be heard to produce intestinal rumbles (borborygmi); heard and smelt to have passed wind (flatus); and seen and heard to pass faeces.

Faeces
Faeces are the undigested residue of the feedstuffs consumed. Even the dry-looking droppings of the horse contain a percentage of water, at least 15% by weight.

The small colon and rectal wall secrete a water-based mucus to lubricate the faeces' passage but the bulk of the water content is that left after resorption of the water in the large colon.

The water content of the digesta consists of:

- that drunk;
- that extracted from the foodstuffs; and
- that secreted by the many glands:
    salivary;
    biliary;
    pancreatic;
    gastro-intestinal wall mucus and digestive enzymes.

During the passage along the digestive tract there is also a two-way (secretion/absorption) movement of water across the gut wall to transport:

- the digested constituents *inwards*; and
- the *exchange* of electrolytes involved primarily in determining the pH level of the different regions of the tract, from stomach to small colon.

This considerable quantity of water, greater than that in the blood and in the extracellular fluids, has to be reclaimed.

The residue of water is a reflection of:

- The water content of the original ingesta, e.g. spring grass gives wetter (softer) faeces.
- The 'health' of the digestive system.

It is recognition of *unusual* consistencies of faeces which is important in horsemanship. Beyond this is the appreciation that the rations fed according to the rules (and eaten) have main-

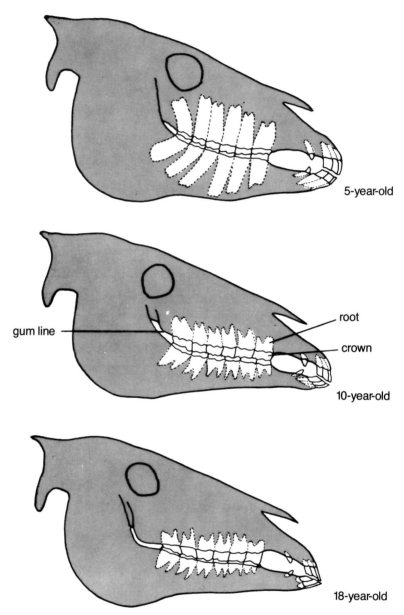

Tooth growth in the horse. The molar tooth root grows until six years old. From the time the crown erupts, this growth pushes more crown through to compensate for natural wear. After six years old the skull (face) and lower jaw bone maintain sufficient pressure on the root to assure crown length. With age the roots diminish.

36

tained the desired condition in the light of work, temperament and weather.

To maximise this end result regular attention should be given to dental care: the 3500 jaw movements per 1 kg (2 lbs) food masticated soon wears the molars to produce sharp points in both upper and lower jaws in stable-fed animals.

Veterinary advice should also be taken regarding a worm-control programme suitable for the particular establishment.

CHAPTER 7

The Rules of Feeding

The rules of feeding are based on scientific fact and it is important for the horsemaster to know and understand them:

1. Feed according to the horse's condition, work and temperament.
2. Feed only good quality foodstuffs.
3. Feed sufficient roughage (fibre).
4. Feed little and often.
5. Make no sudden changes in the type of food fed.
6. Keep to the same times of feeding every day.
7. Feed something succulent every day.
8. Do not work immediately after a full feed.
9. Water should be freely available at all times. Where this is not possible water should be given before feeding.
10. Keep all watering and feeding utensils clean.
11. Know the weight of the volume of food in the stable scoop or bucket so that weight is the basic measurement.

The reasons for these rules are given on the following pages.

1. Feed According to the Horse's Condition, Work and Temperament

It is important that the rations are suitable for the horse in question bearing in mind:

- Present condition.
- The individual's metabolism, i.e. whether he is difficult to keep in condition or puts on weight too easily.
- The work load.

- The ability of the rider.
- Whether extra food is needed for growth.
- His general behaviour.

This subject is discussed in more detail in Chapter 10.

2. Feed Only Good Quality Foodstuffs
It is a false economy to feed poor quality food. Poorly harvested hay or bad oats can cause many problems and these include colic and COPD (chronic obstructive pulmonary disease). Perform- ance will be affected and fussy feeders will reject food.

For competition horses, the higher the level at which they compete the greater the care required in assessing the quality and overall composition of the ration. In terms of performance the ratios of the major nutrients and that of minerals, trace elements and vitamins become critical.

3. Feed Sufficient Roughage
The horse requires plenty of roughage in his diet in order to digest his food properly. Even fit competition horses should never have less than 30% by weight of the ration made up of bulk food. This is mostly hay or its equivalents but also includes chaff.

4. Feed Little and Often
As already stated, the horse is a trickle feeder. If the stomach is overloaded with food some will be pushed into the small intestine without being properly digested. Not only will this be a waste of food but it may also cause colic due to fermentation.

The small size of the stomach (see digestive system) means that not more than 2 kg (4½ lbs) of concentrated food should be given at any one time and part of this should be chaff or soaked sugar beet.

It follows that the total daily concentrate ration must be divided into separate feeds to adhere to this '2 kg (4½ lbs) at a time' rule and the feeds spread as evenly as possible over a working day – a long day may be necessary.

5. Make No Sudden Changes in the Type of Food Fed
Because the bacteria (micro-organisms) in the horse's gut are

'food specific' it is important that any new foodstuff is introduced gradually. Therefore, as an example, horses who do not receive a small amount of bran each day should not suddenly be given a bran mash. A new supply of hay should be gradually mixed with the old supply so the change is not sudden.

When a new horse enters the yard enquiries should be made as to his previous diet. If possible, it should be adhered to and only changed slowly.

When horses travel and compete it is important that all the rations they require are taken with them. A new supply of hay or a different brand of cubes must not suddenly be introduced.

6. Keep to the Same Times of Feeding Every Day
The horse is a creature of habit and will do much better on a regular routine.

Make the timetable suit the yard routine. It is no good arranging for a late night feed unless it can be given regularly every night.

For the one-horse owner who is at work all day the feeds should be given early and late with the horse having plenty of hay to keep his digestion working all day.

Regular feeding times should also apply to horses living out otherwise they are apt to spend much time waiting at the gate.

7. Feed Something Succulent Every Day
Ideally all horses should have some grazing each day. To the horse green grass is the acme of enjoyment. Grazing old pasture will give him the chance to find different grasses and valuable herbs.

Carrots, turnips, swedes etc. are appreciated by the horse, as are apples and other fruit. Carrots are very high in carotene and a good source of vitamin A for horses that are stabled all the time.

Succulents will help to tempt the appetite of the poor feeder and will provide a natural source of minerals and vitamins. Many vitamins are present in fresh, green food.

In the spring, dandelions, both leaves and roots, are much relished by stabled horses.

Some yards now feed 'barley grass'. This is hydroponically grown in a purpose-built cultivator.

8. Do not Work Immediately After a Full Feed

It takes approximately 20 minutes for a horse to eat a full feed and at least 1½ hours to process it through the stomach and small intestine.

Blood is involved in the digestion of food. If there is a simultaneous work effort with muscle activity, the digestion will be impaired.

It follows that if it is necessary to exercise early in the day, either the first feed should be after work or it should be very small. Feed should be given early enough to give time for digestion. This is especially important for competition horses or hunters whose work load is extra demanding.

This rule also applies to the bulk food. Whilst bulk food takes a short time to pass through the stomach and small intestine, it can dwell in the caecum and large intestine for up to 72 hours.

9. Watering – See Part 1.

10. Keep all Watering and Feeding Utensils Clean

Horses are very fussy feeders with an acute sense of smell. All water buckets and feeding utensils should be kept scrupulously clean; all stale food should be thrown away. Food must be kept free of contamination from mice, rats and other vermin.

Some horses will starve themselves rather than eat tainted food.

Warmth and humidity are a suitable medium for micro-organisms to flourish and manufacture toxins. Regular emptying and cleaning of all food containers is essential.

11. Know the Weight of the Food in a Scoop or Bucket

Weigh the empty scoop/bucket, then fill it with each food and re-weigh it. Subtract the weight of the empty scoop/bucket to find out the weight of the food. Feeds can then be measured out in terms of scoops/buckets rather in kilos or pounds.

CHAPTER 8
Composition of Food

Broadly speaking, there are five categories into which the horse's food can be divided. They are:

- Carbohydrate (which includes starch, sugar and cellulose (fibre)).
- Protein.
- Fat/oil.
- Minerals, including trace elements.
- Vitamins.

CARBOHYDRATE

Carbohydrate is a food substance found in vegetable tissue comprising starch, sugar and cellulose (fibre). In the feeding of horses carbohydrates are important and should be the main source of energy for the horse (two-thirds of the weight of the concentrate feed ration should be carbohydrate).

- *Starch* is the major energy store in plants.
- *Sugars* are the simplest form of carbohydrate.
- *Cellulose* (fibre) is insoluble carbohydrate.

Crude fibre contains cellulose, hemicellulose and lignin. The horse can digest cellulose fibre but not lignin.

Fibre is an essential part of the horse's diet: without it he cannot digest his food properly. It stimulates the contractions of the gut. At least 30% of his rations must be fibre.

The main sources of fibre for the horse are grass, hay and straw, which are known as bulk food.

PROTEIN

Protein is a complex organic compound containing nitrogen. Different proteins are formed from varying combinations of twenty-two amino-acids and their derivatives.

Protein is a builder; it is necessary for growth and replacing wastage. It is made up of chains of amino-acids linked together. Some of these amino-acids can be synthesised (made) by the horse. Others are made by the micro-organisms in the gut. However, others known as essential amino-acids must be included in the diet. An ordinary hay/cereal ration is low in these essential amino-acids, so for growing or working horses, additions should be made to the ration.

The most important amino-acid is *lysine*. Two other important amino-acids are *methionine* and *tryptophan*.

Foods that are high in lysine are:

- Peas and beans, including soya bean meal.
- Dried skimmed milk powder (not a suitable source for adult horses).
- Fish meal.
- Lucerne.

Not all high protein foods have easily digestible protein. Reputable compounders making up a mix usually ensure that the protein is digestible.

Some nutritionists maintain that the *total* percentage of digestible protein in the ration should not be over 10% except for lactating mares, foals and young stock.

The protein levels will naturally alter with the changes in the quality of cereal fed. There is no evidence that athletic horses require high protein supplements although individual National Hunt and three-day event horses might. In fact it is thought that the overfeeding of protein to competition horses can be detrimental to their performance.

Composition of Food

FATS AND OIL

All foods will contain some fat/oil as an integral fraction of their composition (i.e. their analysis).

Fat and oil are important for the growth and maintenance of cell membranes, the metabolism of cholesterol and the formation of prostaglandins. They are also used by the horse as a source of energy but, as far as is known, only after metabolism from body fats deposits. Such fat deposits play a role in body thermo-regulation.

Traditional rations are low in oil and many feeders now add corn oil to the diet. When feeding extra oil, vitamin E and/or selenium must be added. (This is one example of a supplement of normal nutrients acting as an antioxidant.)

Dietary fat, in the form of corn oil, is digestible and can reduce the requirements for cereal carbohydrate (starch). Recent studies show that it also lessens the decline in blood glucose during endurance rides and seems to accelerate the recovery of heart and respiration rates during the first 10 minutes of rest.

Since corn oil, along with other oils and fats of plant and animal origin, provides twice as much energy as does starch per gm/oz fed it is a useful part-substitute for cereals in long distance riding and three-day event horses on high rations.

MINERALS (including trace elements)

These are essential elements of the diet but are required in very small quantities. They are inorganic substances.

Macro-minerals
The major minerals are as follows (their abbreviations are in brackets):

- Calcium (Ca)
- Phosphorus (P)
- Potassium (K)
- Sodium (Na)
- Chlorine (Cl)
- Magnesium (Mg)

Micro-minerals
These are the trace elements of importance to horses:

- Zinc (Zn)
- Manganese (Mn)
- Iron (Fe)
- Fluorine (F)
- Iodine (I)
- Selenium (Se)
- Cobalt (Co)
- Copper (Cu)
- Sulphur (S)

Minerals (the usual name for macro-minerals)
Wild horses roaming over large, open areas were able to choose variable herbage and were 'naturally' certain of a reasonably correct intake of minerals in terms of range and quantity. Properly balanced feeding and good pasture management are therefore essential for the domesticated horse's well-being. Supplementation may well be required.

The feral or wild horse, particularly when adult, is not athletic in competition or work terms. The need for high-energy rations is considerably less. Cereals as such will not be eaten and it is cereals which unbalance rations vis à vis minerals. Both minerals and vitamins interact with one another so an imbalance can affect the correct functioning of many body processes.

Adding minerals to the horse's diet should always be carried out with great care. Many of them can be very harmful if given in excess and 'guestimates' of what should be fed may well produce serious imbalances.

Calcium and salt may have to be added to the diet, especially for performance horses and young stock, but magnesium, manganese, copper, fluorine, iodine and cobalt are usually present in sufficient quantities. Sometimes potassium, zinc, iron, sulphur and selenium may be deficient.

Some experts consider that iron may be needed in high-performance horses.

Calcium (Ca) and Phosphorus (P)
These are the commonest minerals in the horse's body and it is

particularly important that they are correctly balanced. They must be supplied in the correct proportions.

Calcium should be present in the diet in a ratio of 2:1, i.e. 2 parts calcium to 1 part phosphorus. Most cereals have a very poor calcium to phosphorus ratio, so seek advice from a reputable feed merchant or from your veterinary surgeon.

Bran inhibits calcium uptake. A calcium supplement, possibly in the form of ground limestone, will be needed if much grain or bran is fed.

Potassium (K)

Potassium is needed for body fluid regulation. It is likely to be deficient in water extracted foods but is high in lush pastures. Well saved forages are higher in potassium than cereals. Supplementation may be necessary when horses are working hard on a high cereal diet but care is required. Molassed sugar beet is a good source of potassium.

Sodium (Na) and Chlorine (Cl)

Sodium and chlorine are also needed for body fluid regulation and are likely to be lost in sweat. The best supplementation is probably common salt.

Magnesium (Mg)

Magnesium is an important element in the blood and in most cellular activities. Its major interaction is with calcium, phosphorus and vitamin D.

Soya-bean meal, good permanent grazing, well made hay and other forages are all good sources of magnesium but most cereals, especially maize, are poor.

Problems such as 'poor performance syndrome' and exertional rhabdomyolysis as part of muscle stiffness, have been shown to be associated with imbalances of these major minerals but *not necessarily* in the rations. Individual animals seem to be unable to make full or correct use of what is present. Veterinary advice based on laboratory findings is necessary before attempting to supplement the diet.

Selenium (Se)

When horses graze pasture which is low in selenium there may be problems and diets should be supplemented with selenium and vitamin E. A deficiency of either selenium or vitamin E can cause muscle disease in young horses. As with most trace elements an excess can be toxic.

Cobalt (Co)
Cobalt may be used in cases of anaemia. It is a component of vitamin B12. A deficiency may cause liver dysfunction or poor appetite.

Copper (Cu)
There are parts of the British Isles where copper deficiency occurs. Copper is necessary for the formation of the blood pigment haemoglobin. A deficiency may cause anaemia or reduced growth.

Macro-minerals play important parts not only in tissue structure but also in metabolic processes and some in the electrolyte balances of intracellular and intercellular fluids.

Trace Elements (minor minerals)
All these play important parts in enzyme action.

VITAMINS

Like all mammals, horses need vitamins, although in very small amounts. Most of these will already be present in the diet of the correctly fed horse, although supplementation may be necessary under some circumstances. Little research has actually been done into the amounts required by the horse although the signs of deficiency are known.

The main vitamins are: **A, C, D, E, K** and the **B complex**.

They can be divided into two groups: fat soluble and water soluble.

- A, D, E and K are all fat soluble and can be stored in the body.
- B complex and C are water soluble and cannot be stored.

Fat-Soluble Vitamins

Vitamin A (retinol) (may be referred to as Beta-carotene)
The horse obtains vitamin A naturally from green herbage which contains carotene. This is converted into vitamin A. There is some carotene present in newly made hay and other preserved grass but this deteriorates considerably with age.

A summer out on good grass will provide enough vitamin A, which can be stored in the horse's liver, to last through the winter.

Horses living in throughout the year and not receiving any green food may benefit from the addition of cod liver oil to their rations, although the amount must be carefully controlled.

Succulents such as carrots, apples etc. also supply some vitamin A.

Broodmares and young stock, particularly newly weaned foals, may also require supplementation.

Retinol occurs in animal fat although a synthetic substitute is made.

Lack of vitamin A can cause anorexia, poor growth, night blindness, inflammation of the cornea, infertility, respiratory disorders. Excess vitamin A is toxic.

Vitamin D (calciferol)
The horse can obtain vitamin D naturally from sunlight on the skin. However, this is limited by: (a) the strength and amount of sunlight; and (b) the amount of time the horse is outside.

The amount of sunlight in the British Isles in winter is probably of little value but the vitamin can be stored by the horse.

A horse living out during the summer will probably accumulate enough to last him well into the winter but thereafter he may need supplementation. A horse that lives in all the time, or is turned out only occasionally, or who is out in a New Zealand rug, will require vitamin D added to his diet. Cod liver oil is a natural source. Synthetic vitamin D can be very potent and needs adding with great care as too much is toxic.

Vitamin D is necessary for the metabolism of calcium and phosphorus. Lack of vitamin D can cause bone and joint problems, as can excess vitamin D.

Vitamin E (tocopherol)
Fresh food such as grains, seeds and herbage are all natural sources of vitamin E. Its levels in stored foodstuffs daily falls as it is 'used' by the foliage and grains as a protection antioxidant. More vitamin E will be needed when selenium is deficient and in an oil-rich diet. Late winter supplementation with vitamin E and selenium may be necessary.

Synthetic vitamin E deteriorates and all compound food and supplements should be date-checked when buying new supplies.

Wheatgerm oil is a good but expensive natural supplement.

Vitamin K
Vitamin K is synthesised by gut micro-organisms. It is also present in leafy matter.

Vitamin K is a blood-clotting mechanism and supplementation is normally unnecessary.

Water-Soluble Vitamins
The water-soluble vitamins include:

- B1 – thiamine
- B2 – riboflavin
- B6 – pyridoxine
- B12 – cobalamin
- niacin (nicotinic acid)
- pantothenic acid
- folic acid
- biotin
- choline
- C – ascorbic acid

Most of these vitamins are either present in high quality food, especially green food, or are synthesised by the gut bacteria. Horses on good quality rations should not need supplementation but horses suffering from disruption of the gut bacteria due to sudden changes of food or antibiotic treatment will need additional supplementation. The important vitamins in this group are thiamine, folic acid and biotin.

Composition of Food

Thiamine is important for horses in hard work as it assists with the breakdown of lactic acid.

Folic acid is high in good grazing, especially that with a high legume content. Stabled horses may be deficient when a form of anaemia may develop. This shows after approximately three months of stabled feeding.

Biotin is thought to be of value for horses with poor hoof formation.

CHAPTER 9

Types of Food

Modern horses' food can be roughly divided into four groups:

- Roughage (bulk food).
- Concentrates.
- Succulents.
- Additives and supplements.

ROUGHAGE (BULK FOOD)

GRASS

Grass is the most natural food for horses. If the quality and quantity are adequate grass is a complete maintenance food from April to September. This is why, if not otherwise organised by man, mares have their foals in late spring.

As the season progresses the energy value falls. In May it may be as high as 12 MJ per kg of dry matter falling in July to 9 MJ (MJ = megajoule – a measure of digestible energy). Sometimes the value may rise again in the autumn. If saved at the optimum time it will supply suitable amounts of fibre, protein and minerals for the resting horse.

Grass is conserved by various means so that it is available as a basic ration throughout the year. The earlier in the spring it is cut the higher the protein value.

It can be saved in the following forms:

- Hay.

Types of Food

- Silage.
- Vacuum packed (as haylage).
- Dried and cubed.

HAY

The most common way of saving grass as hay is to cut it, allow it to part dry in the field, bale it and bring it under cover. However, it may also be 'barn dried', in which case it is baled and carted sooner as hot or cold air is blown through the stack in the barn to complete the drying.

Hay that is grown for sale is usually setting seed and therefore depreciating in food value. It is cut at this stage because the bulk will be larger, the grass more stemmy, and easier to 'save'.

The way the hay is made is of almost more importance than anything else. If it is rained on, this washes out valuable nutrients. It should be dry when it is baled otherwise mould spores will generate inside the bales.

Hay that is not properly dried may become mowburnt. Mowburnt hay is sweet-smelling and a varying shade of brown due to being baled before the sap in the grass has dried. The bales overheat and some stacks can even catch fire. Horses often relish slightly mowburnt hay for its sweet taste, but its nutritional value has been proportionally spoilt.

Judging the value of hay by looking at it is almost impossible. Knowing its 'history' does help. In a large establishment, particularly one with competition horses, it is worth the expense of having the hay analysed. For small establishments or the single horse owner, the cost of a full analysis would be uneconomic, so in this case it must be judged by the following criteria:

- ☐ It should be a good colour. Hay varies from greeny/grey to pale fawn but the greener it is, the better.
- ☐ It should smell pleasant, not musty, nor of vermin, nor mowburnt.
- ☐ It should shake out well and not stick together.

☐   It should be free from dust and disintegrating leaf, especially clover.
☐   It should not have any trace of damp or mould. To test this, it is essential to check the centre of the bale.
☐   It should have a good proportion of flowering heads.
☐   It should be free from weeds such as docks, thistles, nettles, bracken and, most particularly, ragwort. Ragwort, when dried, becomes palatable to horses but it is **very** poisonous, causing liver damage which will eventually result in death.

New Hay
New hay can be harmful to horses. This is because grass made into hay continues to mature chemically in the bale. Although the maturing process uses up some of the sugars, it converts the unwelcome nitrates into amino-acids.

The basic sward from which hay is made is rich in sugars and nitrates. New hay is still maturing and horses fed on it are likely to develop digestive problems. These can result in colic, laminitis and other metabolic disturbances. Filled legs are a typical result.

Hay should not be fed until three months after it has been made.

Two-Year-Old Hay
Two-year-old hay is often sold as 'good horse hay'. It should be noted that it is likely to be worthless in terms of vitamin content, more likely to contain moulds which may be invisible to the naked eye, and will almost certainly be dusty. It is generally better to choose a different forage than to accept old hay.

TYPES OF HAY

Hay can be made from grass or lucerne. It may be specially grown or taken from permanent pasture. Grass hay is usually divided into two types:

• Seed or hard hay.
• Meadow or soft hay.

Types of Food

Seed Hay

Seed hay is made from grass that has been sown specifically as a crop. The grass is usually left down for only one to five years before being ploughed in. It consists of only a few varieties of grass or, in some cases, one variety only. The grasses commonly used are ryegrass, timothy or cocksfoot. Some red clover may be added.

It feels hard to the touch and looks quite 'stalky', hence the alternative name 'hard hay'.

Advantages

- The grass used for the hay will be of a variety that is nutritionally valuable.
- Because it has been grown for re-sale, it is likely to have been made with more care.
- It is unlikely to have weeds in it.

Disadvantages

- Because only one or two types of grass are included, the horse may be limited in mineral intake.
- It is expensive.

Meadow Hay

Meadow hay is made from fields that are down to permanent grass and as a result contain many more types of grass and in addition herbs and possibly weeds as well.

The grasses are usually much finer and shorter in the stalk; thus it is sometimes known as 'soft hay'.

Advantages

- It is made up of many different types of plant, so the horse has access to a wide range of minerals.
- It is less expensive.

Disadvantages

- The optimum time for cutting is difficult to determine as the

grasses flower at different times.
- Weeds, such as docks and thistles, may be incorporated. Worse still, there may have been ragwort in the field.

Clover Hay

Clover hay is seldom seen in Britain as it is hard to make and inclined to break up and become dusty. If used, it should be fed with care as it is high in protein.

Lucerne or Alfalfa

Lucerne or alfalfa is made from lucerne. It is very high in protein and is ideal for young, growing horses, especially if they are working. Many racehorse trainers use it for the two- and three-year-olds in training. It is usually very expensive but less concentrate food will be needed when lucerne is fed. It can, however, be low in phosphates so may need supplementing.

OTHER ROUGHAGE FOODS

Silage

Silage is made from wilted, but not dried, grass and either put into a clamp with the air excluded or sealed in large, airtight bags (known as big bales). It is often made with additives of different kinds. It is important to check that any additives used are suitable for horses. Deaths from botulism after eating big-bale silage have been recorded in horses.

Vacuum-Packed Grass and Lucerne (Haylage)

This is a fairly recent introduction. It comes in small, sealed plastic bags, and to differentiate between hay and silage, the vacuum-packed contents are known as haylage, although there are many trade names. If it is used sensibly, horses seem to do well on it. Haylage is of particular value for horses with respiratory problems.

It is made on the same principle as silage, by excluding the air from cut grass or lucerne. It is important, therefore, to make sure that the bags are not punctured. Mice and rats chewing the plastic can be a problem.

Haylage is usually higher in protein than hay so a horse's concentrate ration should be reduced. The manufacturer should state the protein level. Haylage may have molasses added.

Dried Grass or Lucerne Cubes

These are made from grass or lucerne which has been cut at intervals during the growing season, usually when it reaches about 20 cm (8 ins) high. It is taken straight to a drier and then made into cubes.

It cannot really be classed as a bulk food as it is high in concentrates, both carbohydrate and protein. It is, however, a valuable food and can be mixed with soaked sugar beet to make a mash. The cubes are best soaked before being fed.

Oat or Barley Straw

This can be a useful bulk food in certain circumstances. Its value is often equal to poor hay and, in a bad hay-making year, it is better to feed clean, dry straw than musty, mouldy hay. In this case, however, the horse will need more concentrates as the energy value of straw is low.

Straw can be very useful for ponies, and for horses turned out on rich, succulent grazing. Made into chaff, it can be added to the feed to prevent bolting and to give bulk.

Barley straw used not to be acceptable, as the awns, which are very irritating, were left on the straw. Now combine-harvesting removes the whole top of the stem, leaving only the straw behind.

Chaff

Chaff, or 'chop', is chopped hay or straw. It can be bought ready chopped or cut at home in the chaff-cutter. This is a machine which is operated by electricity or by hand. The machine consists of a long trough with knives at one end, and the hay or straw is fed through the cutters to emerge in pieces about 5 cm (2 ins) long. Proper safety precautions must be taken to prevent accidents.

Only clean, dry hay or straw should be used; oat or barley straw is better than wheat. Beware old, dusty and mouldy material.

56

Not more than a week's supply should be chaffed at any one time. It should be stored in sacks in a dry place as it easily picks up damp from the atmosphere.

Chaff mixed with molasses can be bought, but it is an expensive method of adding bulk to the food. It is, however, useful for horses on a 'slimming' diet as it gives 'something in the manger' and therefore prevents the horse from getting bored or jealous of its companions. Vacuum-packed haylage is dust- and mould-free and can be made into chaff for horses with respiratory problems, but its feed value must be recognised. The same applies to chopped dried lucerne or grass which is also now obtainable.

CONCENTRATES

Seeds contain a high energy store of carbohydrate as starch. Farmers select those plants which carry a high proportion of seed to stem. The harvested crop of seeds is grain and is the additional energy part of the horse's ration.

The amount given should be balanced with the roughage to enable the horse to carry out the work required of him.

Concentrates may be:

- Cereals such as oats, barley or maize.
- Legumes such as peas and beans.
- Other foods such as linseed, fish meal, (milk powder) or sugar beet. Lucerne hay is particularly high in soluble sugars and energy rich cellulose.
- Compound mixtures, made up by a manufacturer to include any of the foregoing. Other foodstuffs may be added, such as minerals and vitamins, but manufacturers are not at present obliged by law to declare the content of their mixtures. Mixtures may be produced as cubes, coarse mix, micronised or extruded.

  A declaration of the analysis of protein, fibre, oil and ash is mandatory, given as percentages. The rest is starch and sugar, i.e. 'energy', and is not legally required to be stated.

Types of Food

CEREALS

These include:

- Oats.
- Barley.
- Wheat (bran middlings and breadmeal).
- Maize.
- Sorghum, rice, millet etc.

The last three are of secondary importance although they may make up part of compound rations.

Cereals are the best providers of carbohydrate energy but the protein they contain is deficient in amino-acids such as lysine and methionine. Cereals are also low in calcium.

Cereal grains may be bruised to make them easier to eat but should not be ground into powder as this reduces their shelf life and makes them less chewable.

Cereal grains can have a 'hotting up' effect. It is thought that this is caused by fermentation by the micro-organisms in the large gut, which causes a rapid rise of glucose and lactic acid. As well as exciting the animals, too much may result in an undesirably high level of muscle glycogen and can be a possible contributory cause of rhabdomyolysis (azoturia) and filled legs. (Pre-cooking is said to reduce these risks.)

Too sudden an intake (e.g. stolen grain) is a common cause of laminitis.

The commerical methods of cooking are:

- Steam pelleting.
- Steam flaking.
- Extruding.
- Micronising.

Extruded grains have been super-heated with steam at 120 °C (248°F) for one minute. *Micronised* grain has been subjected to infra-red radiation. The rapid internal heating causes the grains to swell and gelatinise. The process increases the digestibility of the grain, which is often added to coarse mixes.

All these methods will add to the cost. However, the advantages may include:

58

- Improved palatability.
- Improved digestibility and so avoidance of high starch concentrations in the large intestine.
- Destruction of natural toxins etc.
- Longer shelf life.

Oats

Oats have been the traditional food for horses over the years and are one of the best sources of carbohydrates with a good ratio of starch to protein to fibre. Top racehorse trainers who still feed only oats and hay go to considerable trouble (and expense) to make sure that the feed is of the finest quality, often buying from abroad.

Oats should be plump, clean, sweet-smelling and bushel-weight heavy. The heavier they are, the more weight of kernel to husk. The ratio of weight to bulk should not be less than 0.40 kg:3 dm (40 lb:1 bushel).

They are a safer feed than other cereals in that they are low in density and high in fibre. They can be fed whole to horses over a year old unless the teeth are in need of treatment or the horse is very old.

Oats can be rolled, crimped or clipped. Clipping gives them a lower fibre content. Once treated, they should be used within three weeks as they start to lose their food value.

Oat protein contains slightly more lysine than other cereals. They do, however, have a poor calcium to phosphorus ratio so, if fed alone, must be supplemented by ground limestone or a similar calcium supplement to balance the minerals of the roughage.

Barley

Barley is more readily available than good oats but, as the grain is too hard for horses to break themselves, it must be cracked, crimped or rolled. It has a higher energy value than oats per kg/lb but is consequently lower in fibre and should therefore not form more than half the concentrate ration. Like oats, it has a poor calcium to phosphorus ratio. It can be boiled – see page 108.

Flaked barley has been heat-treated to improve the digestibility of the grain, but the price is usually higher than for other forms of barley.

Types of Food

Maize
Maize is usually fed cooked and flaked. It can be fed whole, although the grains may be too hard for some horses. It is usually more expensive than oats or barley. Its digestible energy is higher per kg/lb than oats but it is lower in fibre.

Wheat
Wheat is not usually fed to horses as grain as it can easily cause digestive upsets. Bran, middlings and breadmeal are by-products of wheat and have been widely used for horses. Wheatgerm oil is a rich, natural source of vitamin E.

Bran
Bran was once one of the traditional foods, along with oats, but its use has now become controversial. The following points should be considered:

- ☐ It is high in fibre.
- ☐ Because it can absorb much more than its weight of water, it can act as a laxative.
- ☐ It is not easily digested.
- ☐ It is very low in calcium and high in phosphorus and phytate. Therefore:
- ☐ The use of large quantities may cause bony abnormalities in young horses and may weaken durability in adult competitive horses as well as upsetting electrolyte levels.
- ☐ It is very expensive.
- ☐ The protein it contains is not of good quality.

If bran is fed, it is essential to balance the calcium/phosphorus ratio in the whole ration.

Breadmeal
Breadmeal has been suggested as a suitable concentrate for ponies as it does not seem to 'hot' them up. It is low in fibre and the calcium/phosphorus ratio needs balancing. It is not a cereal as such.

Linseed
The seed of the flax plant, linseed, is another traditional food for

60

horses. Although it is high in protein and oil, the quality of the protein is poor, being low in lysine. It must always be cooked before feeding so that the boiling inactivates the poisonous hydrocyanic acid which is present in the seeds.

The seeds are extremely hard but are softened by cooking.

If linseed is being fed it should be given daily at a rate of not more than 100 g (3 oz), weighed before cooking.

Linseed can improve the condition of the coat, but as a source of energy there are better types of oil for this purpose.

Cottonseed and Sunflower Seed
These are rich sources of vegetable protein and of value in the feeding of foals and young stock. They are usually processed into compound foods.

SUGAR BEET

Sugar beet is a root vegetable similar in appearance to a turnip or swede. It is processed to extract the sugar (molasses) and the remainder is then made into shredded pulp or cubes. In either form, it is recognised as an extremely valuable food for horses.

It has almost as high a digestible energy as oats but, it does not 'hot' horses up due to the gradual release of glucose into the system. The fibre content is more digestible than most other foods and is of course an additional source of energy.

It is rich in calcium, salt and potassium and, because of this, can be used to offset the cereal imbalance.

Added to short feeds, it will promote digestion by causing the horse to eat more slowly and to masticate the hard food more efficiently. It **must** be soaked before feeding.

It is particularly useful for mixing into dried foods and bulking up rations. Many people use it as an 'opener' (bulk food) in concentrate feeds. It can also be used as a medium to administer medicines, additives and worm doses.

Up to 2 kg (roughly 5 lb) per day can safely be fed to horses. It should be weighed before being soaked.

LEGUMINOUS PROTEIN SOURCES

Peas and English Field Beans
These are both high in lysine and are therefore a useful high-protein food. They should be fed cracked or kibbled and may be cooked. The field varieties grown in Britain are safe for horses and are generally used in compound mixes. The energy value is also high.

Soya-Bean Meal
A meal processed from cooked soya beans. The cooking destroys the toxic substances contained in the raw beans. Soya-bean meal is very high in protein. It is normally used in cubes and coarse mixes although small amounts can be added as a high protein addition to the diet if required.

OTHER FOODSTUFFS

Skimmed milk powder is useful for feeding to weaned foals and young horses up to one year old. It is high in protein, particularly lysine, but contains practically no fat. It is sometimes added to cubes made for young horses. Older horses are unable to digest milk properly.

White fish meal is a rich and valuable high-protein food, containing lysine, minerals and trace elements. It also contains vitamin B12. It is often part of high-protein cubes, especially for foals and young horses.

Brewers' grains are the residue of barley after it has been malted and mashed. It is usually sold dried and can form a useful addition to a horse's ration, but should only be used in small quantities. The grains have a laxative effect when mixed with water.

Brewers' yeast is sometimes fed as a supplement as it is a good source of the B group vitamins. It is said to have a calming effect, but is very expensive.

Lawnmowings are not safe for horses as they compact and heat up very easily when placed in heaps. (Ponies gaining access to such garden dumps are liable to severe colic and/or laminitis.)

Cut grass, provided it is long and has been scythed, is safe provided it is fed immediately it has been cut. Only a small amount should be given to horses who are not already receiving a daily supply of grass.

Hydroponic (barley) grass is a means of producing a daily supply of fresh green food. Soaked barley seed is placed in trays in a controlled warm, damp, well-lit environment and the 'grass' is ready for feeding in a few days. Not all horses like it but it can be a useful way of providing fresh 'grass' all the year round.

Molasses is unrefined black treacle. It is much relished by horses and is a good vehicle for masking the taste of unpleasant substances such as medicines, worm doses, calcium etc., which have been added to the feed. It is now included in many processed foodstuffs.

Tit-bits such as Polo mints or sugar cubes are relished by horses and, used in small quantities, will do them no harm, apart possibly from teaching them to nip! Chocolate-based tit-bits should not be given to competition horses as they contain banned substances.

Carrots, apples, cabbage leaves and pea pods are often appreciated by horses which live in all the time and they will do no harm in small quantities. Carrots in particular are rich in carotene and make a valuable addition to the diet.

Branches and prunings from the garden will be enjoyed by horses (and more particularly ponies and donkeys), being more naturally grazing *and* browsing animals, especially when they are living out and the grass is rich and lush. The varieties offered should be chosen with care: no evergreens should be included, nor poisonous shrubs like laburnum and box. Beech, lime, sycamore and rose prunings are all safe and much liked.

Turf is a useful source of grass for stabled horses and many people, including racehorse trainers, cut a turf of grass about 30 cm (1 ft) square for each horse in their care every week. The whole turf is offered – grass, roots and earth – and is usually entirely eaten. The turf should be put on the ground in a corner of the box.

Herbs

Herbs will be selected by horses from whatever grazing is available. Usually these herbs are high in valuable minerals and especially trace elements. When land is re-seeded for grazing horses, it is recommended that a strip be sown with herbs.

Dried herbs can be mixed into the horse's food. If minerals have been added to dried herbs, it is necessary to check the balance of the ration.

Garlic is usually fed as a powder and is more readily accepted by horses when mixed with molasses. It is useful for horses with respiratory problems and is said to be helpful in the control of sweet itch. Its regular use is effective as a fly repellent. It can be used to disguise the taste of medicines.

Comfrey is known as the 'healing herb' and has been used for many years. It is the only plant known to metabolise vitamin B12 from the soil. It has a high content of easily absorbed calcium.

Dandelions, both leaves and roots, are much relished by horses. They are high in minerals and vitamins.

Nettles, if cut and allowed to dry, are often appreciated. They are a good source of minerals, especially iron.

Seaweed is said to improve the condition of bad doers. It is high in iodine so the amount used should be carefully monitored. The nutrients are 'organic'.

COMPOUND FOODS

These are a mixture of foodstuffs chosen by the manufacturer and presented in different forms.

- **Cubes** are made from selected foods, which are ground up, steamed and pelleted. They may contain any variety of mixes to make them up to the stated protein, oil, fibre and ash levels.
- **Coarse mixes** may be anything from plain cereal mixes to high protein mixes containing soya-bean meal, peas and beans. The contents may be rolled, flaked or micronised. Molasses or corn syrup is usually added to make them very palatable.

Compound foods generally contain added minerals and vitamins. Unfortunately, it is not always possible to find out exactly what raw constituents are in a compound mix. Manufacturers (understandably) often alter the constituents according to availability and cost.

Compound foods include:

☐ A *complete* mix, usually in cube form, which is said to need no hay added to the diet.
☐ A cube mixture of concentrates and supplements to be fed with hay. These usually start with about 10% protein – sometimes called 'Horse and Pony Cubes' or 'Country Cubes' – and work up through 14% protein for competition horses, 15% protein for broodmares to 18% protein for foals.
☐ A concentrate mixture as a coarse mix, to be fed with hay.
☐ A combination of two or three foodstuffs such as lucerne and barley, to be fed with hay.
☐ A fibre mixture as an alternative to bran, chaff or sugar beet, to be mixed with other foods.
☐ A balancer to be fed with oats or other cereals.

Compound foods for competition horses must be free from prohibited substances.

There are some foods, such as 'Racehorse' and 'Event' cubes, which are regularly tested and made under rigidly supervised conditions. Reputable manufacturers realise the importance of these tests and are insured against claims. *The onus remains with the horse's owner/trainer*, however.

When selecting a compound food, always check the details on

the bag. If a horse is receiving only the compound food as well as hay, there should be no need for supplements. However, if part of the concentrate ration is straight food, it may be necessary to work out if any supplement is needed to balance the ration. Some vitamins, such as vitamin E, lose their potency after a time and, if one is included in the compound mix, it is important to check the manufacturer's 'use-by' date.

SUPPLEMENTS

The horse owner is at present deluged by manufacturers advertising all sorts of mixtures to add to horses' and ponies' feeds.

If horses in medium work are being fed their concentrate ration as a compound food plus good quality roughage they should require nothing extra except possibly salt (NaCl).

Horses on home-mixed diets should have their rations checked. Many such diets are low in salt and calcium so competition horses should certainly have salt added to their rations and may need calcium, lysine and methionine. Vitamins A, D, E and folic acid may be necessary in the winter or where horses are permanently stabled.

However, vitamins and minerals cannot be considered in isolation. There are complicated interactions between them and between other nutrients, especially between vitamin D, calcium and phosphorus, and vitamin E and selenium, and the B-vitamins and carbohydrates. The specific manipulation of vitamin levels in the diet should only be undertaken with professional guidance. Many of these interactions are not yet clearly understood or identified.

Supplements include:

- Minerals including trace elements.
- Vitamins.
- Herbs.
- Bacterial cultures (Probiotics).
- Miscellaneous.

Reputable manufacturers of compound food will incorporate the necessary minerals and vitamins in their products and provide details of their analysis. Horses living out on land known to be deficient in some minerals will need supplements unless bought-in feeds contain the specific minerals.

Salt

Salt may be given by any of the following methods:

- Rock salt in the manger.
- Salt-lick on the wall.
- Added to the feed.
- Salt block in the field.

There are advantages and disadvantages to all methods.

Rock Salt in Manger

Advantages

- It is cheap to buy.
- It stops horses from bolting their feed.

Disadvantages

- Horses may not gnaw at it every time they have a feed and so will not ingest sufficient salt.
- Metal feed pans become corroded.

Salt Lick on Wall

Advantage

- Salt is always available.

Disadvantages

- Some horses do not use it.
- It is very messy on walls and tails.
- Empty holders can be physically dangerous.
- There is a danger of infection if horses with coughs and colds are moved from box to box.

Salt Added to Feed

Advantage

- The amount given can be monitored.

Salt Block in Field

Advantage

- It is readily available.

Disadvantages

- Some horses may not use it.
- If placed on the ground it will eventually dissolve and kill the grass on which it lies.
- It needs a special non-metal holder, with drainage holes; or it can be hung on a fence, thereby limiting the grass damage.

Probiotics

Probiotics are supplements designed to promote the perform-ance of the existing digestive micro-organisms and also to add to their number. They are now used, under guidance, to assist in the better use of the food fed to some horses.

Their usefulness and perhaps their risks are not yet fully evaluated. It is wiser not to consider them as a supplement but as a therapeutic or prophylactic medicine.

Similarly with:

Antibiotics, including those used against ringworm which are 'in feed' medications. Horses on antibiotics may have to be given extra vitamins. This is because oral antibiotics can kill the good 'bugs' in the gut. The horse will take some time to build up the flora. During this time some degree of indigestion may occur.

CHAPTER 10

Deciding on a Ration

Art Versus Science

Although the science of horse feeding has increased with new-found knowledge, it is important not to forget the practical aspects.

Weighing or measuring horses can be very useful, but nothing quite takes the place of the person who, just by looking at his horse, can alter its feeding a little to keep it in top condition. This takes much practice. The changes in amount should still be done by weight.

It is useless saying that the horse must have X amounts of this and Y amounts of that if (a) the horse does not look or do well on it; or (b) he does not like the food.

Two horses of the same type and size both eating identical rations may look completely different because one is a good converter of food and the other a bad one. This is where the practical horsemaster comes into his own.

It is almost impossible to give exact amounts of food for different horses doing different jobs. For example, it is possible that one three-day event horse may be fit to run for his life on 5 kg (11 lbs) of concentrates while another of the same size and type may need 9 kg (20 lbs). However, *as long as the horse is not losing condition* it is better to under-feed than over-feed.

Deciding what to feed can seem very complicated to the more inexperienced person. The simplest way of doing this is to decide on a maintenance ration by considering the horse's size, age and type. Then it is necessary to work out what energy ration the horse will need to carry out its task, either for work or growth or both.

Deciding on a Ration

The tables on pages 80 and 123–4 give a guide and the approximate amount of the concentrates the horse will need can be calculated from them. It is then necessary to decide on the type of concentrates, bearing in mind their energy and protein value.

Maintenance Rations
A maintenance ration is the food that is necessary to keep the horse that is not working in good condition. This does not cover broodmares and growing young stock as they need extra food, for late pregnancy and lactation in the former, and growth in the latter, all functions which are in fact 'work'.

A maintenance ration may be made up from grass in the spring and summer, or from hay and sugar beet in the winter with some additional food as necessary.

Beware additional feeding of non-working horses at grass in some autumns and early winters. All factors must be taken into consideration.

GENERAL CONSIDERATIONS

The following considerations should be taken into account when deciding on a ration:

- Present state of condition and health.
- Size and type.
- Age.
- Weight.
- Amount of work.
- Temperament.
- Ability of rider.
- Weather (is horse out by day, day and night, or only for exercise?).
- Economy (cost-effectiveness).
- Availability of foodstuffs.
- Feed storage and handling facilities.

Condition
The condition of the horse is assessed by using a scoring system.

This measures the weight distribution over the neck, back, ribs and quarters.

Fat should not be confused with muscle bulk, or vice versa. Often, apparent muscle bulk is, in fact, excessive fat which has 'hardened', such as on the crest of ponies or overweight stallions. (NOTE: When, standing relaxed, the horse's muscle, when palpated, feels soft and pliable.) Contrary to popular belief, fat will not turn into muscle with work.

Horses vary in their bulk of muscle, and the type of work they do can also influence their shape. For example, the muscle fibres in the horse trained for stamina and endurance, such as a three-day eventer or long-distance horse, are less 'bulky' than those of a sprinter, dressage horse or show jumper. The fit eventer will look lean and streamlined, whilst the show jumper will have a more rounded appearance.

The muscle groups in a fit horse are clearly delineated.

Excessive weight puts unnecessary strain on the heart, lungs and limbs, and can shorten the useful working life of the horse or pony.

Condition scoring

Score 1   Starvation level. Croup (sacral) and hip bones (pelvis) prominent and very sharp, especially over points. A marked hollow in front of the withers. A very deep temporal fossa and possibly a sunken eye. Spinous processes of the vertebrae are well defined. Rib cage prominent with all ribs showing from behind foreleg muscles. Skin tight.

Score 2   Ribs easily visible. Contour sunken either side of backbone. Spinous processes will defined. Quarters sunken, with pelvis and croup points well defined. Deep depression under and either side of the tail. Bones palpable.

Score 3   Withers, croup and backbone processes and points still clearly defined. A little more muscle definition but still hollow in front of the wither. Slight cavity under the tail.

71

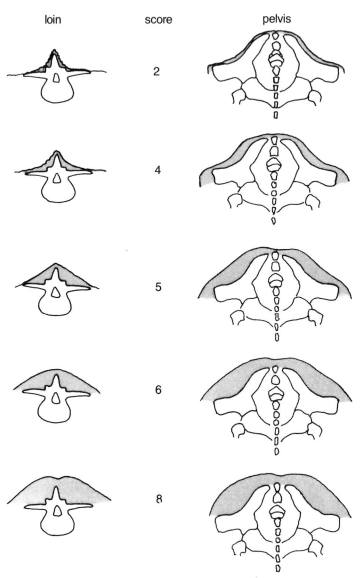

loin	score	pelvis
	2	
	4	
	5	
	6	
	8	

Condition scoring – judged visually from behind and above and by palpation. Shaded areas are flesh masses, with variable thickness of fat between muscle and skin. In the horse most 'points' except the buttocks (tuberischii) are not covered by muscle. Fat is, however, deposited between the skin and the bony prominences (points) but never to any extent.

Score 4   Front half of rib cage covered, back half still visible. Neck beginning to fill up in front of the wither. Spinous processes still palpable.

Score 5   Approaching normal for degree of fitness or rest. Withers, croup and hip bones palpable with pressure but some muscle definition developing.

Score 6   Normal. Firm, muscled neck. Ribs just covered but palpable. Haunch, croup bone and buttocks covered but easily felt. Muscles well defined.

Score 7   Beginning to carry too much weight. Slight crest development. Ribs well covered, requiring firm pressure to palpate. Pelvis and croup well covered.

Score 8   Fat. Definition of bones, except at points, lost. A hollow gutter from croup to tail. Neck becoming hard and cresty.

Score 9   Obese. Ribs, quarters and back buried in fat. Deep palpation necessary to feel croup and hip bones. Loaded shoulder fat, and beginnings of a hollow from wither to croup.

Score 10   Very obese. Marked crest. Neck very wide and firm. Deep hollow from wither to tail. Back broad and flat. Huge pads of fat on shoulders and quarters. Pelvis and croup buried. Skin distended. Lumbar region 'raised'.

Size and Type

Size and type should be considered together, as the more 'common' type of animal, although heavier, will usually have a better food conversion rate than the more thoroughbred type of horse.

Deciding on a Ration

Size (height and weight)
The height and weight of the horse can provide a guide to feeding. Determining the height is not a problem. To discover the weight the following methods can be used:

- Weighing the horse on a horse weighbridge.
- Driving the horsebox or trailer on to a public weighbridge with and without the horse.
- Using a specially calculated equine weigh tape (available from tack shops and feed merchants).
- Calculation using the following equation:

$$\text{Weight (kg)} = \frac{(\text{girth})^2 \times \text{length (cm)}}{11900}$$

Girth is measured around the barrel immediately behind the elbow, after the horse has breathed out. Length is measured from the point of the shoulder to the point of the buttock.

Once body weight of the horse has been determined, it is important to decide whether the animal is overweight, under-weight or showing a lack or loss of muscle tissue, i.e. wasting.

As a rule, weight loss or gain relates to too much or too little body and subcutaneous fat. If wasting is obvious, or if an animal is plainly obese, weight as such is of little consequence. Over-feeding or under-feeding of the average conditioned horse has no (immediate) effect on muscle mass.

It has been suggested that for the resting horse, i.e. one on a maintenance ration, 1½% of body weight is required in food; for light work, the horse requires 2% of his body weight in food, and for medium to strenuous work from 2.5% to 3%. Young horses and pregnant mares in the last three months of pregnancy need between 2.5% and 3% as dry matter weight. However, these rough guide percentages depend on the type of food supplied. Horses do vary in the use they make of their food according to their type and individual metabolism. There is also a minimum requirement of 1% of the body weight as long fibre for correct gut function.

Age
The age of the horse will have a bearing on the rations chosen.

74

Young horses who are working as well as growing will need more food to cover the extra requirements for carbohydrate and protein.

Older horses may also require extra rations, but this can be decided by assessing their condition. Very old horses whose teeth may be poor or who are living out and taking very little exercise, will require an easily masticated and digestible ration of high quality food. Old horses who are unable to graze properly or to keep themselves warm should never be left out in the winter. Keepers of these horses should appreciate that it is far kinder to have them painlessly destroyed than to allow them to linger on when they are not happy and cheerful.

Temperament

Placid, easy-going horses that 'take little out of themselves' will be easy to feed but must not be over-fed and allowed to get fat. They are likely to turn extra 'energy' food into fat rather than energy. However, it is important to differentiate between naturally 'laid-back' horses and those with an illness or suffering from a deficiency. Any alteration of temperament requires investigation.

Horses with a difficult, excitable temperament can be a problem to feed as they lose condition through excessive energy expenditure. Giving them more food to replace lost condition can often make them more excitable. They require plenty of roughage and are usually better on energy foods that do not contain too much cereal, i.e. sugar beet and lucerne.

The Weather

The weather must be considered when deciding on the amount of food that horses require. Food is used to maintain body temperature. In very cold weather horses will use more food to keep themselves warm. This is particularly so for clipped horses. If no extra food is given they will use stored fat and thus start to lose condition.

Under-fed horses, because of loss of insulating fat, will more readily lose body heat by radiation and convection and will, of course, feel cold. This results in shivering and further energy expenditure.

Food as such does not produce heat, but the act of eating does produce muscle activity heat. The cellular work necessary for digestion, absorption and metabolism and other vital activities are all heat-producing.

It is the risk of loss of body fat in cold weather which necessitates extra winter feeding.

Economy (Cost-Effectiveness)
Unless funds are unlimited, price must be considered when deciding what foodstuffs to buy. This is especially true for commercial establishments. However, it is false economy to feed poor quality food, however cheap it is. It is cheaper in the long run to buy sensibly and so avoid ill-health costs. However, equivalent value foodstuffs should be costed and compared in price.

The length of time taken to make up complicated feeds should also be considered, especially in a large commerical yard. Moreover, mistakes in mixing and serving are more likely.

Availability of Constant Supplies of the Same Quality
This particularly applies to hay, and, to a lesser extent, cereals such as oats or barley. If storage is available, enough forage should be bought to last for several months. If not, arrangements for storage may be made with the supplier, but this, of course, will make the food more expensive.

If compound foods are bought it is important to ensure that further supplies will be available when required.

Supplementing the Ration with Grazing
Some daily grazing will benefit the horse's health but will make the balancing of rations more difficult. The quality and quantity of grass will fluctuate with the seasons and this must be taken into consideration. The richness of the spring grass can easily lead to feeding too much protein and carbohydrate, with too little long fibre. Conversely, winter grass has lots of long fibre but little in the way of carbohydrate and protein. The possibility of infestation by the various forms and degrees of parasitism must also be considered.

Ease of Handling

The considerations here are:

- The staff.
- The layout of the feed and hay shed.
- Access.

Other points might include:

- ☐ Size of bales.
- ☐ Size and weight of bagged concentrates.
- ☐ Movement of loose food (such as oats).
- ☐ Time taken to bring food to feed shed.
- ☐ Time taken to make up feeds.

HOW TO CHOOSE WHAT TO FEED

The main points to consider when choosing what to feed are:

- Energy.
- Protein.
- Fibre.
- Calcium/phosphorus ratio.

Measuring the Value of Foodstuffs

Food should always be fed by weight. The weight of a 'scoop' of oats or cubes should be known. As an example, a scoop of oats will weigh less than a scoop of cubes. Hay or vacuum-packed grass should be weighed before being fed unless it is being fed *ad lib*, i.e. to appetite.

The nutritional *value* of the food should also be known; straight foodstuffs such as oats, barley or hay can vary enormously in quality and for competition horses it is worth having these analysed.

The value of the food is expressed as:

- ☐ The digestible energy (DE) of the food.
- ☐ The crude protein.

Deciding on a Ration

☐ The Ca/P ratio.
☐ The vitamin and mineral content.

Concentrates made up by food manufacturers have their values listed on the label and these should not alter, although the actual constituents may vary in amount owing to the economics of the market.

Digestible Energy

Digestible energy (DE) is computed in megajoules (MJ). (A joule is a measurement of energy. Energy is expressed as the number of joules in a kilogram of food. Because there are so many joules in a kilogram they are measured in megajoules.)

For example, if oats are to be measured they are likely to have digestible energy levels of around 14 megajoules per kilogram; this is written as DE = 14 MJ/kg. (See Table 3 on page 125.)

As a rough guide for maintenance, a horse or pony needs 18 MJ of digestible energy plus an extra 1 MJ for each 10 kg of body weight. For work, add 1–8 MJ for each 50 kg of body weight, according to how hard the horse is working. Add extra MJ for lactation, pregnancy and growth, as shown later. Thus a 500 kg horse doing 1 hour of work per day (including cantering and jumping) requires:

$$18 \text{ MJ} + \frac{500 \text{ MJ}}{10} + 4 \times \frac{500 \text{ MJ}}{50} = 108 \text{ MJ DE/day}$$

i.e. maintenance + work = energy required.

Protein

Suggested percentage of protein in the total ration:

● Light work 7.5–8.5%
● Medium work 7.5–8.5%
● Hard work 8.5–10.0%
● Strenuous work 8.5–10.0%

Adult horses not above 10% in total ration including roughage.

Suggested protein percentages required for broodmares and young stock:

☐ Pregnant mares: 8–10%.

- ☐ Mares in last three months of pregnancy: 11–13%.
- ☐ Lactating mares: 14% gradually decreasing to 12%.
- ☐ Foals not receiving enough milk or spring grass: 16–18% in a compound ration. On good grass with sufficient milk from their dams no extra food is necessary. (Thoroughbreds will require special consideration, especially if bred for flat racing.)
- ☐ Weaned foals 6 months old: 14.5–16%.
- ☐ Yearlings 12–18 months old: 12–14%.
- ☐ Two-year-olds: 10–12%.
- ☐ Three-year-olds: 8.5–10%.

NB There is some evidence that over-feeding foals and yearlings may cause epiphysitis and/or contracted tendons. The significance of excess protein, excess energy and/or imbalanced minerals is not yet resolved but must be important as distinct from just one nutrient being blamed.

Work
The work the horse is required to do, the rider he has to carry and his own temperament all have to be considered under this heading.

Work per day
Work can be defined, on a scale of 1 to 8, as follows:

Category	Scale Point	Activity
Light work	1	1 hour walking.
	2	Walking and trotting.
Medium work	3	Some cantering.
	4	Jumping, schooling, dressage, driving.
Hard work	5	Eventing, cross-country driving, hunting, endurance riding.
	6	Hunting 2 days a week, three-day eventing.
Fast or energetic work	7 8	Racing.

A guide to feed requirement for work		
Work category	**% Hay**	**% Concentrates**
Maintenance	100	0
Slow light work	85	15
Light work	80	20
Medium slow work	70	30
Medium work	60	40
Hard work	40	60
Race training	30	70

The above is an approximate guide and must be altered to suit the horse. However, the 'bulk food' ration should *never be less than 30%* of the total ration. If other types of roughage are used in the place of hay, the concentrates may well have to be decreased.

A horse at rest will require only a maintenance ration but if the horse is working, not only is it necessary to feed the horse so that he has enough energy for the job, but also so that he remains sensible enough to carry it out without harming himself or his rider.

An Example of Practical Application in Deciding a Ration

Size, type and temperament
Fred is a 15.3 hh, ⅞ths-bred horse with a good temperament. He weighs 500 kgs (1100 lbs).

Age
He is 8 years old, so has stopped growing.

Health
He is in good condition, has been blood-tested, is regularly wormed and has his teeth done.

Work
He is required to take part in local riding-club competitions at weekends (these do not include fast work). He goes for a short hack daily. His rider is of average ability.

Economy
He must be fed well but not extravagantly.

Ease of handling foodstuffs
His one-horse owner, who has a job, finds ready mixed compound food easy to deal with.

Availability of constant supplies
This has been checked with the feed merchant. Enough hay to last the winter has been bought.

Does part of the ration come from grazing?
Fred is occasionally turned out for a short time when he is not ridden. It is autumn and as there is little grass at this time of the year, it is not added to the diet sheet.

Weather
As it is autumn and it is not yet cold, Fred is trace-clipped and wearing a rug. The weather at the moment will not affect the ration.

Having considered all the above points the ration is worked out as follows:

☐ Because he weighs 500 kgs (1100 lbs) it is estimated that he needs about 13 kgs (29 lbs) of food daily (2½% of his body weight).
☐ Because of the work he is doing he probably requires a concentrate/roughage ratio of about 25% to 75%, or roughly a quarter of his ration in energy food made up with threequarters of hay.
☐ His suggested ration might be:
2.6 kg (6 lbs) Horse and Pony cubes @ 10% protein.
0.5 kg (1 lb) sugar beet weighed before soaking @ 9% protein.
9.5 kgs (22 lbs) quality hay at about 8% protein.
☐ As a compound food has been used no extra supplementation should be necessary.
☐ According to condition, behaviour and the work being done the ratio of concentrates to roughage may be altered.

CHAPTER 11

Rations for Different Types of Horse

HORSES LIVING OUT AND NOT WORKING

A horse who lives out and is not working requires maintenance rations, i.e. it must be given enough food to *maintain* it in good condition.

Spring and Summer Maintenance

From May to October grass is an adequate ration for all horses and ponies **if in sufficient quantity and quality**. Native ponies may need their grazing restricted if the grass is very good, owing to the danger of laminitis. All stock benefit from additional long fibre when on lush grass.

If the grazing is limited, or of poor quality, supplementary feeding will be necessary.

Winter Maintenance

Horses and Thoroughbred type ponies will require supplementary feeding. The grass will have little feed value and they will need food to keep themselves warm. Oats, sugar beet with a mineral/vitamin supplement and hay *ad lib* is a suitable ration. A ratio of between 10% to 20% concentrate to 90% or 80% hay should be adequate, but a careful watch should be kept on the animal's condition. Winter coats can easily disguise any loss. If an 'oat balancer' (a concentrate mix specially made to feed with oats) is fed with the oats no mineral supplementation should be required as this will contain the necessary minerals.

Native ponies grazing on a sufficiently large area may not need any extra food but those on restricted or possibly horse-sick grazing will need hay. In years when hay is difficult to obtain, clean oat straw and sugar beet is an acceptable alternative.

COMPETITION HORSES

The horse in hard competition work will require more energy food than the same horse in medium work. However, it should be appreciated that each horse will have a level of required-energy food and feeding above that level will not produce extra fitness. Food does not create fitness.

The fittening chart on page 123 should be studied, but note that fitness can go on increasing after the level of food remains the same.

It used to be thought that horses doing strenuous work required considerably more protein than other horses. This has been found not to be so. The level of protein in the whole diet should not add up to more than 10%. (National Hunt and three-day event horses may, as individuals, benefit from a determined amount of extra protein such as from soya.)

The rations for competition horses doing fast or energetic work are all very similar although the type of work is often very different.

Blood-testing at the beginning of the fittening programme and then again when the horse is fit, is a sensible investment. Some successful racehorse trainers test as often as once weekly.

Competition horses on a restricted hay ration become less bored and digest their food better if their bulk food is chaffed.

Prohibited Substances
Racehorses in Britain and horses running under FEI Rules anywhere in the world may be tested for prohibited substances. This also applies to some national competitions. It is therefore very important that these substances do not get into horses' food by mistake. Contamination usually occurs during transit or at the milling plant. Cocoa is the most likely contaminant.

83

EVENT HORSES

Event horses should be fed so as to maintain trained muscle bulk without becoming fat, yet so that they have enough energy to do their work in a sensible economical way. Feeding them so they are jumping out of their skins is not only a waste of food but may cause them to injure themselves or their riders.

Keeping them on a very low hay ration can cause them to run up too light and may cause digestive problems.

Event horses are subject to doping rules, so if they are fed cubes or a coarse mix it is important that the supplier is prepared to state that these products are free of prohibited substances.

Event horses need very little extra protein. The normal rules for feeding should apply and the **total** protein ration should not go above 10%.

Advanced, energetic competition horses should have their hay/roughage analysed and properly balanced rations made up in conjunction with quoted or determined analyses for concentrates and supplements.

Novice event horses are often given too much concentrate food. They are not being asked to do a great deal and should be fed according to the rules based on the recommendations given earlier. Most novices do not need more than 2½–4 kg (6–9 lbs) of event cubes of, say, 11% protein, plus hay. For some horses this may have to be stepped up or for others decreased.

Advanced three-day event horses probably do not need more than 4½–6½ kg (10–14½ lbs) of concentrates. Several Badminton winners have had less than this. Too much concentrate food can result in toxicity problems and the horse refusing his food. Feeding *per se* will not produce fitness: this must be built up through work. The energy spent must be replaced by appropriate feeding.

Horses must be watched to see they are not losing condition and the ration adjusted accordingly.

Two possible example rations for 16.2 hh event horses weighing 600 kgs	
Example 1	**Example 2**
Oats 4 kg (9 lbs)	Event cubes 6½ kg (14½ lbs)
Sugar beet 1 kg (2¼ lbs)	–
–	Hay 6½ kg (14½ lbs)
Vacuum-packed	–
grass 6½ kg (14½ lbs)	
Grazing 1 hr	Grazing 1 hr
Supplements including	–
calcium	
Salt (amount depending on	Salt (1–2 tablespoonsful,
supplement content)	according to sweating)

The amount should be varied according to fitness, condition and behaviour.

The roughage part of the ration should not be less than 40%.

Roughage/concentrate ratio		
	Roughage	*Concentrate*
Novice eventer	75% to 50%	25% to 50%
Advanced 3-day eventer	50% to 40%	50% to 60%

LDR HORSES

Long-distance riding horses need more energy than any other type of competition horse. Although they are not working at high speeds they have very long distances to cover at a consistent speed.

These horses must not be allowed to become fat. They should be very well muscled, but without the round outline of the dressage horse or show jumper, and should carry no excess weight.

They require easily digestible high energy food with not too much bulk food. The addition of oil (such as corn oil) to their daily ration may be of benefit. Usually 100 ml (2–3 fl oz) is fed but much more has been given successfully.

Roughage/concentrate ratio
60% to 30% Roughage: 40% to 70% Concentrates

If a grain diet is fed a broad-based mineral supplement should be given. This should not be given with compound foods as they already have added vitamins and minerals. If oil is fed the supplement should have a high vitamin E and selenium content. Salt (100 mg) given daily is important. Long-distance horses lose water and electrolytes since they sweat for much longer (distance/time). NaCl (salt) are two of the electrolytes lost. More advanced horses will benefit from a more comprehensive mixture of minerals (precursors of electrolytes) but specialist advice should be taken.

The following rations have been recommended by successful long-distance riders.

Horse working 2 hours daily but not yet competition fit	
Bulk (hay etc.) *ad lib* Oats rolled Barley micronised or flaked } Sugar beet	2½–3½ kg (6–8 lbs) daily
Possible additions:	25–50 ml (1–2 fl oz) corn oil 25 g (1 oz) salt mineral supplement

Lucerne pellets and straw are better than poor hay.

LDR horse competing
Between 3½–6½ kg (8–15 lbs) concentrates and roughage to balance, possibly made up as follows: 6½ kg (15 lbs) best quality hay   2 kg (4½ lbs) oats   1½ kg (3½ lbs) barley   1 kg (2 lbs) hunter cubes   Sugar beet, soaked   75 ml (3 fl oz) corn oil   Mineral supplement

DRESSAGE HORSES

The dressage horse needs to produce slow power and does not need speed (it must be fit for this job but must not carry too much fat). It must be sensible and obedient, yet have enough energy for the job. The more advanced the training the more energy the horse will require. Dressage horses, like hunters, have to remain fit throughout the whole season, so a careful check must be kept on their condition and behaviour.

Overleaf is a typical home mix diet for a 16.1 hh, six-year-old, threequarter Thoroughbred/quarter British warmblood of Advanced level, being worked hard for approximately an hour a day by an international rider.

16.1 hh Advanced dressage horse

---

7 kg (16 lbs) hay
1 kg (2¼ lbs) rolled oats
1 kg (2¼ lbs) micronised barley
1 kg (2¼ lbs) coarse mix 12% protein ⎫ Guaranteed free from
1 kg (2¼ lbs) cubes 12% protein ⎭ prohibited substances.
½ kg (1 lb) sugar beet
Broad-based supplement with additional salt and vit E.
1 hour turned out in field

Total: 11½ kg (26 lbs)

Roughage/concentrate ratio approximately 60%:40%

POINT-TO-POINT HORSES

Getting the point-to-point horse fit for racing is rather different from getting other horses fit because the point-to-pointer will have been hunted and will be fairly fit but may well be rather lean. After hunting he may benefit from being let down slightly for one to two weeks with slow exercise. During this time he should be on reduced rations but not if it is judged that he requires to put on some fat before serious fittening starts. (See also Book 5 – *Specialist Care of the Competition Horse.*)

Because he is now partly fit his feeding can start as at the sixth week with a ratio of 50% roughage:50% concentrate.

The traditional method of feeding point-to-point horses was good quality oats and hay. This is still practised with much success. However, it is suggested that if this diet is chosen an 'oat balancer' and some sugar beet should be added. Salt and a general-purpose supplement will help to make up for any deficiencies in the diet.

If compound foods are preferred it is important that they are free of banned substances.

By the time he starts racing the horse should be on a ratio of 40% concentrates:60% roughage or even 35%:65%.

SHOW JUMPERS

Show jumpers are required to make a considerable muscular effort for a short time. They need to stay fit for a good length of time as the season is now very long.

When horses are travelling for so much time it is sensible to feed compound foods. This will mean that it is necessary to carry only one kind of concentrate food and hay.

It is important that feeding times are carefully adjusted to fit in with jumping times.

POLO PONIES

Polo ponies have to work very hard and fast for short intervals. They need to be muscularly, very fit and need high energy food to enable them to achieve this.

Because of the usual time of play, the afternoon, the feeds on playing days need adjusting. Polo ponies should be fed four times daily if possible – morning, early lunch, tea and late night.

On a non-playing day the larger feeds should be lunchtime and late night. On a playing day only a very small feed should be given at lunchtime. Hay should be given first thing in the morning and taken away at least three hours before playing.

Any pony who stops eating should have his mouth carefully examined. Owing to the severe bitting used on some ponies there may be damage to the mouth which will make it reluctant to eat.

Usually cubes or coarse mix are more suitable than a straight cereal ration as although polo ponies need to be very fit they must be sensible.

HUNTERS

Hunters should be fed the same sort of rations as event horses but with more bulk food. They require between 3½–5½ kg (8–12 lbs) of concentrates and good hay. Thoroughbred horses need hay or bulk food *ad lib* but the usual rules still apply.

They must be fed so that they are well behaved, can gallop for short distances, and remain out of their stables all day, probably for three days in every fortnight from November until March. Once fit it is not easy to keep them looking and feeling well throughout the season. Their rations will need careful adjustment so that they do not lose condition. A late night feed, if it can be given regularly, can be of great benefit.

On rest days after hunting, their concentrate ration should be reduced and their roughage ration increased. They should be walked out and, if possible, grazed in-hand.

Traditionally a bran mash was given after hunting, but nutritionists now consider this to be contra-indicated. (See bran mashes, page 107.)

RIDING-SCHOOL HORSES

In this case economy has to be a prime consideration. It is essential to shop around and compare the prices and contracts that are available from feed merchants and farmers. Large discounts are often offered for yearly contracts. However, low cost must not be the only criterion. The horses and ponies must look well, their manners must be impeccable and they must stay healthy.

Good, clean, affordable hay is the basis for feeding riding school horses; good hay will lower the necessity for large quantities of expensive concentrates. Meadow hay is usually cheaper than seed hay and if well saved is just as nutritious. In years when good hay is scarce and very expensive, alfalfa pellets fed with clean oat straw make an acceptable alternative.

Most commercial riding schools have found that horse and pony cubes provide the best type of energy food. These cubes are low in protein and high in fibre and are ideal for animals doing two to three hours of slow work daily. They will already contain the necessary supplements. Soaked sugar beet, although sometimes difficult to manage in large quantities and rather messy, is a good non-heating addition.

It is impossible to give amounts of food without knowing the weight, size, type and the work the horses are going to do. If students are being trained it will be necessary for them to experience the use of some other kinds of foodstuffs – possibly these could be used for special liveries or any competition horses at the school.

THE 'ONE-HORSE OWNER', NON-COMPETITIVE HORSE

For the one-horse owner whose animal is not going to do anything very strenuous it is sensible to choose a reputable manufacturer and feed their compound food, either as cubes or mixture. In this way all the necessary nutrients will be automatically included in the diet. Usually manufacturers are apt to be too generous in the quantities of food that they suggest for the various sizes and types of animals, so, as always, it is necessary to consider the condition of the horse and its behaviour.

Between 70% and 80% roughage should be fed, as little energetic work is being done.

CHILDREN'S PONIES

It is of prime importance that children's ponies are fed so that they are quiet and sensible. They should look well but their manners are of paramount importance.

They can be divided into groups and then divided again as to the work they are doing.

Group 1 – The small woolly native pony, such as the Welsh or Dartmoor types.

Group 2 – The larger native pony, such as Highland, Dales, Fells and Welsh cobs.

Group 3 – The more finely bred pony, such as Connemara, Arab or Welsh riding ponies.

Group 4 – The Thoroughbred or nearly Thoroughbred pony.

All these groups blend into one another but it should be remembered that Groups 1 and 2, the native ponies, are much better converters of food than their aristocratic cousins. If being fed with the pony's weight as a guide, Groups 1 and 2 will probably only require 2% of body weight.

The ever-present danger of laminitis in over-fat ponies in Group 1 must be kept constantly in mind.

Groups 3 and 4 will need about 2½% of body weight. The roughage/concentrate ratio will depend on the other factors already discussed in Chapter 11 but particularly on the work they are doing. This can be divided into:

- **Beginners' ponies** – Whatever their size, as long as they have sufficient roughage, they usually require little or no concentrate. If it is necessary to give them a tit-bit to catch them or some food in the stable so that they are anxious to come in, this should be a small handful of the lowest possible energy food. If they start to lose condition, the roughage should be increased or some sugar beet and dried grass or alfalfa added. The last should not make them excitable and will help to put condition on again.
- **Family ponies** – The energy food required will depend on the amount and kind of work being done. Their concentrates will probably be between 5% and 20% of the total ration. A compound mix of about 10% protein is most useful.
- **Riding-school ponies** – Those working between two and three hours daily may need between 10% and 20% of the total ration fed as concentrates. Their concentrates are likely to be whatever is fed to the other school horses.
- **Hunting ponies** – Those living in at night and hunting every Saturday may need between 15% and 30% of their total ration as concentrates. A compound mix is better for them than a ration based on oats.
- **Competition ponies** – These may vary from top-class JA jumping ponies to show ponies in lead rein classes and their rations must depend on the type of competition for which they are used.

It must be remembered that cereals such as oats have a hotting-up effect. A horse and pony type of mixture is a safe food. It will contain a reasonable amount of fibre and have all the necessary vitamins and minerals added. Soaked sugar beet pulp is a good source of digestible energy and does not have the same hotting-up effect as the cereals.

MARES, FOALS AND YOUNG STOCK

The general care of mares and foals is covered in *Book 1, The Horse.*

Mares
Although pregnant and nursing mares should be well fed with good quality, easily digestible food they should not be over-fed. The size of the foal is determined by the genes from the sire and dam and not by the amount of food the mare is given. A higher protein ration should be given in the last three months before foaling (especially if foaling early) and while the foal is on the mare. If the grass is very good this extra protein may not be necessary.

Foals
The feeding of the foal should depend on the response of the foal to the dam's milk. Some mares give a large quantity and others very little. In the latter case the foal should start eating concentrates as soon as possible.

Early weaning may cause a loss of condition so foals who are to be weaned early should be eating well and will have to have their energy and protein ration increased when they are taken away from the mare. Foals who are weaned at five to six months should need little extra if they are eating concentrates and grazing. Mares who are not in foal again may be allowed to run on with their foals. As the mares dry off they will wean the foal themselves when they may be separated with little trauma.

A balanced diet must be fed to growing animals if their full growth potential is to be reached whilst achieving healthy bones and teeth. Incorrect or over-feeding of foals may cause epiphysitis or contracted tendons. A good appropriate pre-mixed feed, specially prepared for young stock from a major horse feed manufacturer and fed at recommended levels, is really the most efficient way to feed foals and young stock. Foals cannot digest whole oats and need quality foods suitable for their limited digestive ability. Due to the immature nature of the foal's hind gut, proteins produced by the gut flora in the adult are not available to the youngster.

Young Stock
Young stock will require supplementary feeding from August right through to the end of April, and possibly longer if there is little grass. They need extra protein for growth and carbohydrates for maintenance. They should be fed so that they always look well covered but not too fat. Too much protein may cause lameness problems. Their diet must be well balanced with sufficient minerals, especially calcium, to ensure steady healthy growth.

Young stock, particularly weaned foals and yearlings who are living out in the winter, will require extra feeding to make up for the loss of condition through adverse weather conditions. Given sheltered conditions and good grazing they can be left out until the end of December and then brought in at night until the weather starts to improve in the spring. However, even Thoroughbreds, provided that they have enough proper food and available shelter, will do perfectly well kept out all the time. The disadvantage is that they do not have daily handling and may object strongly when they are eventually brought in. Whether they are in at night or out all the time, good hay, sugar beet, stud cubes of about 14% protein, plus a good supplement will provide a good ration.

Growing horses require a higher level of protein than mature horses and the younger they are the more they will need.

STALLIONS

Stallions may be divided into two groups:

- Those used only as stud animals.
- Those that are ridden or competition animals as well as used at stud.

Stallions Doing Stud Work Only
Stallions should be on a rising plane of nutrition as the stud season (spring) approaches. During the season and depending on the number of mares they are to cover, they should have high energy food but must not be allowed to become fat. When the season is over they should be let down gradually and returned to a maintenance ration.

Stallions Being Ridden and Used at Stud
Sometimes the competition stallion is 'retired' to stud for the season and afterwards continues with his ridden work. In this case, depending on the work that he has been doing there is usually no necessity to change the rations. However, if the ratio of roughage to concentrates is altered the foods should remain the same. For the stallion who continues to do his ridden work as well as his stud work, his concentrate ration will have to be increased.

In all cases, the condition and behaviour of the stallion will determine the necessary changes that should be made.

CHAPTER 12

Feeding Problems and Non-Routine Feeding

Sudden Refusal of Food
If a horse who usually eats normally, refuses to eat, it may be a sign that something is seriously wrong with the horse.

Should refusal persist for more than two feeds, especially if hay is also refused, the veterinary surgeon must be called. If other signs of illness appear, this professional help should not be delayed.

However, there are other reasons such as:

- Stress.
- Over-feeding.
- Lack of clean, fresh water over several days.

} Horse shows little desire for food and won't eat.

- Contaminated food.
- Dirty feeding utensils.
- Acute tooth problem, sore mouth, tongue etc.

} Horse will usually show desire to eat.

In the absence of clinical illness check on the above.

'Bad Doer' (Thin Horse)
A bad doer is the horse that eats all he is given but does not look well. The more common reasons are:

- Worms.
- Sharp teeth.

- Lack of adequate food.
- Poor quality food, especially hay.
- Unbalanced diet.
- Poor metabolism, often caused by being incorrectly fed or starved in the past.
- Over-stress.

The bad doer should be checked by the veterinary surgeon.

There are serious reasons for horses being thin or losing weight. They include:

- ☐ Heart abnormalities.
- ☐ Chronic pain.
- ☐ Anaemia.
- ☐ Ragwort poisoning and other liver pathologies.
- ☐ Cancers.
- ☐ Kidney disease.
- ☐ **Worms** (internal parasites). *See Book 2: Care of The Horse* and consult your veterinary surgeon.

The Sick Horse
It is essential that veterinary advice is taken when there is doubt about diagnosis and especially treatment.

Illness can be acute or chronic. The acute form could be colic, sudden viral infection or something resulting in a high temperature. The chronic form could be liver damage, anaemia, or cancer of some part of the digestive system. Some of these can be diagnosed by blood-testing.

The veterinary surgeon will advise on a ration in cases of acute illness.

Recent work suggests that feeding certain types of fats may stimulate healing mechanisms.

For ill and convalescent horses, feeding little and often is of prime importance. Any food not eaten within ten minutes must be removed. Containers must be washed with plain water between each feed. Many sick horses prefer to eat from the ground.

They require nourishing, easily digestible food and should not have large quantities of cereal-type food. Anything that they are prepared to eat is generally the answer, and molasses is often of assistance to tempt them. Some *freshly* cut grass, if it is available, is usually acceptable and many horses enjoy dandelions, which are full of minerals. Chopped dried lucerne is often appreciated and is a valuable food.

A mash may be made of soaked, dried grass cubes and sugar beet.

Enforced Rest

For fit horses who are going to be off work for perhaps only two or three days, halve the concentrates the first day and on the third day halve them again. Give more roughage and cut out any oats after three days, then adjust down to maintenance rations by the seventh day.

Horses who have to be kept stabled with no exercise for some time, perhaps from lameness, should be given a maintenance ration with no additional energy food. They must have all the necessary minerals and vitamins to aid recovery, and the diet must be sufficiently laxative. Hay or its equivalent plus sugar beet and some additives should be sufficient. A slight loss of condition is of less importance at this time than the maintenance of a calm attitude.

Stress

Excessive stress may result in loss of condition.

The causes of stress can be:

- Strange stable.
- Disturbance in yard.
- Poor handling.
- Travelling.
- Pain.

Discover and minimise the cause as far as possible. Give most of the food at night. If this is only a short-term problem, do not worry; although the horse may run up a bit light he will not be harmed by not eating very much for two or three days.

The horse suffering from long-term stress may show this by weaving, box walking or other stable vices. He needs to be kept in a quiet box and have a strict work and feed routine. A slightly larger, late-night feed, which he can digest quietly, may be of help. The more he can be turned out, even if the grass is poor, the better.

Travelling (See also Chapter 5, Dehydration)
Water and food should always be carried and enough time should be allowed for stopping to water and feed the horses en route. They should be given time to finish their feeds before proceeding. Some horses will not eat when on the move and there is a risk of choking should they do so.

When travelling very long distances, such as across Europe, care must be taken during the journey that the food is easily digestible and is not likely to cause metabolic upsets. The quantity of concentrates should be halved and the roughage increased. Extra electrolytes may be necessary.

It is essential when travelling abroad to find out what feed is and is not allowed into the countries that the horse is travelling through.

PROBLEMS AND AILMENTS CONNECTED WITH DIET

There are several ailments that may be directly caused by incorrect feeding and others on which incorrect feeding may have a bearing. They include:

- Under-feeding.
- Over-feeding.
- Colic.
- Diarrhoea.
- Azoturia.
- COPD.
- Electrolyte losses.
- Anaemia.
- Choking.
- Lameness, including laminitis.

Problems and Non-Routine Feeding

Under-feeding can cause:

- ☐ Starvation – resulting in death.
- ☐ Chronic malnutrition.
- ☐ Weakness and inability to work.
- ☐ Deformity of bones in young horses.
- ☐ Stunted growth in young horses.

Over-feeding can cause:

- ☐ Bone disorders in young horses – mainly epiphysitis. (See feeding young horses, page 93.)
- ☐ Contracted tendons in young horses.
- ☐ Reduction of fertility; problems in foaling mares.
- ☐ Problems in strenuous exercise owing to carrying excess weight.
- ☐ Lameness from added strain on the legs and feet.
- ☐ Inability to carry out proper work.

The over-feeding of concentrates is particularly common with event horses, who may suddenly go off their food. The answer is to cut the concentrates by half for one day and by another half the next day and then gradually alter the diet so that the quantity and balance are correct.

Colic

The word 'colic' simply means abdominal pain of some sort. It may be severe, sudden or gradual in onset, or of a low level of pain. There are many different kinds of colic and many causes, including those listed below:

- ☐ Incorrect feeding, i.e. wrong times, variations in type, wrong amounts.
- ☐ Wind sucking, which may cause indigestion.
- ☐ Mouldy food.
- ☐ Poor teeth.
- ☐ Too large feeds.

It is now accepted that feeding mistakes are less commonly the cause of colic but the risk should not be ignored. A sudden

100

change to cereals will readily produce large gut acidosis producing electrolyte imbalance, bacterial proliferation and colic as well as laminitis.

A sudden change to long fibre is more likely to induce colonic impaction.

Diarrhoea
Can be caused by:

- ☐ Worms.
- ☐ Stress.
- ☐ Oral antibiotics.
- ☐ 'Upset' micro-organisms in the gut, due to sudden change to cereal or lush grass feeding.

In all cases of diarrhoea there will be dehydration, particularly in acute cases. Fluids containing electrolytes may be required. Veterinary advice should be sought; this is particularly important in the case of foals, and in adults if it persists for more than 24 hours, or less if general signs of illness are present.

Azoturia, Monday Morning Disease, Set Fast, Tying Up
These are all names for more or less severe symptoms of the same process. *Equine rhabdomyolysis* is the name used to encompass the whole syndrome. This may range from muscular cramp to actual degenerative changes in the muscles.

It is usually associated with exercise after a short period of rest on full rations, thus the name Monday morning disease. Symptoms may range from stiffness and soreness in the muscles to a refusal to move, severe sweating, high pulse and respiration rates and the horse in obvious pain.

The horse should not be moved and veterinary assistance should be sought immediately. Permanent damage to muscles can occur if the horse is moved.

Mares are said to be more prone to azoturia than are stallions or geldings.

Horses should always have their concentrate ration reduced on their rest days and should be warmed up slowly before work and allowed to unwind gradually after fast work.

101

The following have all been suggested as possible predisposing factors:

- ☐ Faulty metabolism.
- ☐ Vitamin and/or mineral deficiencies.
- ☐ Hormone abnormalities.

Some success has been achieved in the treatment of constantly recurring rhabdomyolysis by feeding extra calcium and/or salt.

Feeding a Horse with Wind Problems (COPD)

This horse will almost certainly be allergic to the fungal spores in hay and straw and also to dust. As far as possible he should live in a dust-free environment, be bedded on shavings, sawdust or paper. His food should be chosen or treated so that he does not inhale any mould spores or dust. The bulk food should be either hay that has been immersed in water for half a day or vacuum-packed grass. He should be fed on cubes and sugar beet and if other food is fed it should be damped. Good ventilation is of prime importance (see Book 6, *The Stable Yard*). He should be taken outside to be groomed and for mucking out. The more he can be outside, the better he will be. The addition of garlic to the ration has proved beneficial in some cases.

When travelling, straw should not be used on the floor of the vehicle and the hay nets of any travelling companions should also have been soaked.

Lameness

Lameness which can be caused by incorrect feeding includes:

- ☐ Laminitis.
- ☐ Epiphysitis.
- ☐ Contracted tendons.
- ☐ Poor hoof formation.
- ☐ Lymphangitis.

These are described in *The BHS Veterinary Manual*.

CHAPTER 13
Preparing Food

The means by which horses are fed are important. Food is expensive and it should be carefully stored and prepared so that none is wasted.

HAY

Hay can be fed:

- ☐ Loose on the ground.
- ☐ In hay net.
- ☐ In hay mangers.
- ☐ In hay racks.

Loose

Advantages

- Natural for the horse to eat off ground.
- Labour-saving.
- Safe.

Disadvantages

- Difficult to soak but can be tipped out of soaking net.
- Difficult to weigh but slices of a known weight bale can be measured off reasonably accurately.
- Wasteful.
- Untidy in yard.

Hay Nets

Advantages

- Economical.
- Can be prepared in advance.
- Easy to weigh.
- Tidy to handle.
- Easy to soak.

Disadvantages

- Time-consuming in labour, and if soaked, difficult to lift unless a pulley is fitted.
- Can be dangerous, especially in young-stock boxes.
- Expensive to buy – poor 'life'.
- Unnatural eating position.

Hay Mangers

Have the same advantages and disadvantages as loose hay on the floor. They may be less wasteful.

Hay Racks

Due to the possible danger of hayseeds entering the horse's eye there are reservations about the use of hay racks, particularly those which are high.

Feeding Hay

All staff handling hay which is visibly mouldy or very dusty could wear masks as a precaution against 'farmer's lung' disease. (NB: Such material should not be used anyway.)

Soaking hay

Mould spores. Certain horses are allergic to the mould spores found in hay, straw and chaff. These spores are a danger to these horses, not because they are eaten and swallowed, but because they are inhaled. All hay and straw contains some spores, but visibly mouldy products contain considerably more. Horses fed and/or bedded on mouldy material run a greater risk of inhaling more spores than the natural mechanism of their respiratory system can cope with. Sooner or later some spores reach the bottom of the airways (alveoli). Although the healthy horse may be able to cope with this, in the allergy-prone horse a disease state is stimulated.

It is advised that such horses should be fed soaked hay. Soaking hay keeps the spores' surface tension high and so prevents them from escaping from the eaten fibre into the airway. They are masticated and swallowed and do not enter the lungs. An alternative school of thought suggests that soaked spores swell to become too big to gain access to the sensitive alveolar area. When exhaled they are wiped off on to the throat and then swallowed. It must be appreciated that the welfare of a known COPD horse should be discussed with a veterinary surgeon.

Soaked hay. The prevalence of allergic coughing has encour-aged the feeding of soaked hay. This is hay soaked in water for about half a day before being fed to the horse. The easiest method is to put the hay into a net, which is then immersed in a tank of water. The hay net is then hung up and allowed to drip before it is given to the horse. It should not be allowed to dry right out. Another advantage of soaking is that it washes out much of the dust, which in many horses causes 'hay cough'. However, it may also remove soluble nutrients, so be prepared to feed a vitamin/mineral supplement and good quality feedstuffs.

In a large establishment where all the hay is soaked (a sensible precaution) a long tank not more than 1–1.25 m (3–4 ft) high is essential. The morning hay nets are put in overnight and the night nets put in at mid-day. The nets are lifted from the water and allowed to drain before being hung up. They are very heavy and a pulley system saves the staff considerable strain.

In a one-owner yard a dustbin makes a suitable receptacle for soaking. When travelling, boiling water poured on to hay in a plastic sack will be better than nothing as it will at least lay the dust, but it is better to arrange soaking, even if for a short time.

All hay should be weighed before being soaked.

Feeding hay loose on the ground or in a manger
Hay to be fed loose should be shaken up and placed on a sack

105

that has handles at each corner. The sack can then be picked up by the handles, weighed on a weight hook and carried directly to the horse's box. Hay should not be carried loose in the yard; it is both wasteful and untidy.

Feeding in hay nets. The hay should be shaken up and then put into the nets; these are then weighed. Some yards colour code the nets so that if they are prepared in advance they do not need to be re-weighed. Several nets can be carried to the boxes at one time.

Nets, either full or empty, should never to left on the ground. Bad accidents have been caused by horses getting caught up in nets. In the box they should be hung as high up as possible and tied with a quick-release knot.

Hay nets are unsafe for foals and young horses, who should be fed loose hay on the ground.

Concentrate Feeds

The correct mixing and preparing of concentrate feeds is important. All equipment must be kept clean and washed before fresh food is mixed.

Soaking Sugar Beet

Cubes must be soaked in cold water for 24 hours. Flakes and pulp must be soaked in cold water for at least 12 hours. They should be put in a bucket and just covered with water. Sufficient water should be used to make them soft without making them very liquid. Hot water should not be used as it will cause the beet to ferment. In cold weather the soaked beet must be protected or it will freeze. In hot weather it should be covered and kept in a cool place. Fresh supplies should be mixed daily, especially in warm weather, as fermentation will occur if beet is left soaked. Any surplus liquid should also be used up.

'Openers'

It is good practice to mix all compound or grain food with an 'opener', usually sugar beet or some form of chaff. Openers have the effect of making the horse chew his food more thoroughly and eat more slowly.

Sugar beet
The beet is soaked and mixed with the remainder of the concentrate feed. Once mixed it should be fed immediately.

Chaff
In the past all stables were equipped with a chaff cutter through which hay or good quality straw was passed. It was cut into short lengths and a double handful was mixed into each food.

In the absence of a chaff cutter (and modern safety regulations now make this an expensive piece of equipment) it is possible to buy chopped hay or straw mixed with molasses. This is an expensive method of adding chaff but for the one-horse owner or in special circumstances it may well be worth it.

Short-cut molassed grass or lucerne
This comes already chopped. It is usually a high protein product (12%–16%) and although it will improve the digestibility of the food, it may also alter the protein and energy levels adversely. It requires careful assessment and balancing with the other foodstuffs.

Grass or lucerne cubes
These will probably have a similar value to the packed short-cut material but will not be as useful in making the horse chew and eat more slowly. Some makes of these cubes need soaking so it is important to read the instructions on the bag.

Mashes
In the horse world it has been traditional to give horses a bran mash the night before a rest day or after strenuous work. Modern nutritionists now consider this practice to be contra-indicated for the following reasons:

- There is a sudden change of diet with which the gut bacteria cannot deal. Until these bacteria have re-established themselves the new rations cannot be fully utilised.

- A mash which is based on bran is not a balanced food.

If, however, some bran is fed every day, a bran mash will not have such a detrimental effect as the gut bacteria are accustomed to it.

Mashes can be made from bran, barley or linseed, dried grass cubes or sugar beet.

Making a mash

A **bran mash** is made by putting the required amount of bran in a bucket and pouring sufficient boiling water on it to form a crumbly consistency without being wet. It is then covered and left until cool enough to feed, which usually takes about 20 minutes. Salt and a handful of rolled oats or flaked barley may be added to make it more palatable.

A *linseed mash* is made in the same way as a bran mash but the liquid from cooked linseed is substituted for the boiling water. (See cooking linseed, below.)

A *barley mash* is made by pouring boiling water on to flaked barley in the same way as for a bran mash. Alternatively, whole barley is cooked in water until it is soft and fed when cool.

If the horse is accustomed to having some grass cubes and sugar beet, an acceptable mash can be made from them. It is prepared by soaking the grass cubes and sugar beet in the usual way and then mixing them together. A tablespoonful of salt may be added.

Cooking

To cook oats or barley

These may be cooked in a boiler designed for the job or boiled in water in a large pan. It is important that sufficient water is added to prevent burning, but not so much that all the goodness is lost in the water. The grain should feel soft when pressed between finger and thumb and should have absorbed most of the water. Salt may be added.

To cook linseed

The seeds should be added to boiling water to make sure that the enzyme linase is destroyed before it has time to release the poisonous hydrocyanic acid, which is in turn destroyed by boiling. It is important that plenty of water is used; when cold this will form a jelly. Linseed burns and boils over very easily, so needs careful attention while cooking. Once the seeds have come to the boil, the heat may be reduced and the seeds simmered for 4–6 hours. The cooked seeds and jelly are added to the feed when cold. Alternatively, the hot liquid may be added to bran to form a linseed mash.

Oatmeal gruel

A double handful of oatmeal is put into a bucket and boiling water is poured on while stirring vigorously. It is then left to cool. Sometimes a handful of sugar is added to make it more palatable.

CHAPTER 14

The Feed Shed and Storing Food

Feed Shed Layout

In the layout of the feed shed the following points should be considered:

- Saving time.
- Cleanliness.
- Storage.

Time

Feeding, especially in a large establishment can take up a lot of time. It therefore makes sense to design a layout that is as labour-saving as possible. Everything should be easily to hand.

Cleanliness

The feed shed should be easy to keep clean, in the interests of hygiene and appearances. It should be possible to sweep the floor easily without having to move any of the contents. The walls should be smooth and easily dusted. Shelves should be of painted wood or melamine.

Storage

Storage of concentrates

All types of concentrates can deteriorate if kept in poor conditions. Ideal conditions are:

- Low temperature.

- Little or no variation in temperature.
- Low humidity.
- Good ventilation.
- No direct sunlight.
- Protection from infestation by rats, mice, birds, insects and mites.

Suitable containers are:

- ☐ **Metal bins**, which should be raised off the floor on small wooden blocks.
- ☐ **Plastic dustbins** – these hold about one 25 kg bag of feed.

Storage of vacuum-packed forage
Because these bags are airtight, the storage considerations are rather different from those of other foodstuffs. Under no circumstances must the bags be punctured.

It is important to protect the bags from:

- Rats and mice, who chew the plastic.
- Sharp edges, which may puncture the bags.
- Sunlight.

Storage of salt
Salt absorbs moisture from the atmosphere; it is therefore important that it is kept airtight.

It is usually bought in plastic bags and, even when opened, it is sensible to keep it in its bag inside a container such as a dustbin. A week's supply should be taken out at a time and kept in a large plastic jar. Do not leave it in contact with metal as it is corrosive.

A melamine or plastic spoon should be used for measuring.

Storage of hay etc.
Even well-saved hay deteriorates with age but good storage conditions will keep it palatable for a longer time. The important points to consider are:

- Protection from weather.

- Protection from damp, especially from the ground.
- Good ventilation.
- Protection from vermin such as rats and mice.

It should be stacked with small gaps between the bales and, if possible, raised on pallets.

A cheap, open-sided lean-to barn is a better way of storing hay than covering it with plastic sheets; the latter, having no ventilation, will encourage multiplication of whatever mould spores are present. Large round bales, although more difficult to deal with, take much less harm from the weather than small rectangular ones.

Equipment in the Feed Shed

Feed containers

These may be **buckets**, which are then emptied into mangers, or **feed pans**, which are given directly to the horse.

Buckets should be fairly heavy-duty 10 litre (2-gallon) size with names or numbers on them. These can be painted on or put on with Dymo tape.

The contents should be emptied into a more suitable manger in each loose box.

The advantages of using buckets are that they are:

- Easy to keep clean.
- Easy and light to handle.
- Easy to store by stacking.

The disadvantages of using buckets are that:

- Some food is liable to be left and wasted in the bucket.
- The feed is more difficult to mix.
- Buckets may be piled inside one another without checking that the bottoms are clean.

Feed pans should be difficult to knock over yet not too heavy.

Their advantages are:

- All the mixed food goes straight to the horse.

112

- Owing to their large size the food is easy to mix.
- They can be fitted into a rubber tyre which prevents bruising and tipping over.

The disadvantages are:

- They can be difficult to keep clean.
- They are bulky to store.
- They must be removed from the boxes after the feed is finished. This can be a problem with late night feeds. Rubber bowls as distinct from metal ones are not so dangerous but even these can be stood in and kicked up, bruising cannon bones.
- They can be difficult to label.

Water
It can be useful to have a tap and a drain either inside or just outside the feed shed. This can be used for washing utensils, for providing water for soaking sugar beet or for damping feeds.
   Large establishments will also benefit from a sink.

Power point
This should be well away from the water supply and should be used with a circuit breaker. A power point can be useful for boiling a kettle or for a linseed or barley boiler if used.

Kettle
An electric kettle can provide hot water for washing. If used it must comply with up-to-date requirements for safety at work.

Cupboard
This is essential for storing small items and medicines that are currently in use. It should be fitted with a lock and be out of children's reach.

Scales
It is essential that scales are large enough to hold the contents of a scoop. Fold-up, hanging wall scales are tidy and unobtrusive. Spring-loaded balances are required to weigh hay.

The Feed Shed

Feed chart
A large blackboard with permanent lines and columns should be in an easily read place on the wall.

A shelf
A separate shelf for supplements, additives, oil, etc. is advisable.

Other useful additions are:

- ☐ *A damp proof container* for salt.
- ☐ *Scissors or snips.*
- ☐ *Knife.*
- ☐ *A big mixing spoon* for molasses etc.
- ☐ *A ml measure* for medicine.
- ☐ *A dustpan and brush* for cleaning out bins.
- ☐ *A short soft broom* for sweeping the floor.

A feed trolley
In a large yard this can be a valuable piece of equipment. The buckets or feed pans can be placed on the trolley and the food then put directly into them. The trolley can be wheeled along the yard to the boxes. If a trolley is used, there should be a ramp into the feed shed instead of a step.

Appendices

APPENDIX 1
Rationing

This appendix is for those who like to know some of the theory and science behind the practice.

Nature is both economical and well balanced so it provides plants that are complementary to animals. Plants store the sun's energy and animals use it to drive their body processes and provide movement. Plants build up natural elements into proteins; animals rebuild these to form their own structure. When devising rations we must be particularly concerned with energy and protein.

In the wild, the horse selects the foods he needs; in domesticity we must provide the right quantity of a suitable mix of foods, particularly for the stabled horse. This is the art of rationing. As already shown, this is achieved partly by experience, partly by observation and partly by careful thought based on sound theory. However, it is normally based on simple calculations which once done, create a starting point from which later changes can be made. Also, calculations allow different foods to be compared so that the ration is not too costly.

The following rationing system for horses (shown overleaf) involves six simple steps.

EXAMPLE 1

STEP 1

How big is the animal? Measure or estimate (see page 74).

STEP 2

How much can it eat each day? (See page 74 and the table on page 124). Allowing, say, 2.5% of his body weight, divide the weight of the horse by 100 and multiply the answer by 2.5. A 500 kg horse will thus eat 5 × 2.5 = 12.5 kg (about 28 lbs).

STEP 3

Provide for maintenance using mostly grass, hay or other forage (see page 70). This amount varies according to the quality of the food; so calculate what is needed first, then divide that amount according to the quality value of the food proposed and thus find the weight of forage needed. The unit used is Digestible Energy, measured in megajoules (expressed as MJ of DE). As shown on page 78, a horse or pony needs 18 MJ of DE plus one more MJ for every 10 kg of his body weight.

Thus a 500 kg horse needs 18 + 50 = 68 MJ of DE. To provide 68 MJ from our average hay which has 9 MJ per kg (see table on page 125), divide 68 kg by 9. Answer = 7.6 kg (about 17 lbs) of hay is needed for maintenance. (For fast work provide some of this in concentrates to keep the horse slim.)

STEP 4

Provide concentrates for work. As shown on page 78, provide 1–8 MJ of DE for each 50 kg of body weight. In selecting between 1 and 8 use the scale points of work as shown on page 79. For example, a 500 kg horse in medium work on scale point 4 needs 10 x 4 = 40 MJ of DE to provide enough energy for its work. If this is provided by horse and pony cubes which have a DE of 10 MJ per kg (see table on page 125) then 4 kg (about 9 lbs) of cubes are needed.

STEP 5

Check the protein, check the hay/concentrate ratio and check for capacity.

The table on page 78 suggests that medium work needs 7.5–8.5% of protein in the total ration. The table on page 125 shows that the hay has about 8% protein and the cubes will have 10%. This gives a ration of 8.6% protein – a little over but near enough.

A ration consisting of 7.5 kg of hay and 4 kg of cubes has a ratio of 65% hay and 34% concentrates. (The table on page 80 suggests a slightly higher percentage of concentrates for medium work so consider this in Step 6.)

Step 2 showed that the horse could comfortably eat 12.5 kg. Thus if we are providing 7.6 kg of hay and 4 kg of cubes, making a total of 11.6 kg, we are well within its capacity and can give more if it seems appropriate.

STEP 6

Feed this ration, observe, consider and adjust as necessary.

EXAMPLE 2

Here the system explained in Example 1 is applied to a 16.2 hh advanced event horse.

STEP 1

Weigh the horse on the local feed merchant's weighbridge (using a trailer, then subtracting the weight of the empty trailer). He weighs 600 kg.

STEP 2

Capacity at 2.5% of body weight = $\frac{600 \times 2.5}{100}$ = 15 kg (34 lbs).

STEP 3

Provide for maintenance = 18 + $\frac{600}{10}$ = 78 MJ of DE needed.

Supply only 40% of capacity from hay: 15 × 0.4 = 6 kg (13.3 lbs). Our good hay has a DE of 11 MJ per kg, so 6 kg × 11 = 66, leaving (78–66) 12 MJ still needed.

STEP 4

Provide for production. Our horse is on scale point 6 (hard work).

$\frac{600}{50}$ × 6 = 72 MJ of DE

Add the 12 MJ still needed for maintenance:

72 + 12 = 84 MJ of DE

Feed, say, eventing cubes at DE of 13 MJ = 6.5 kg (14 lbs).

STEP 5

Check the protein level:

6 kg of good hay at say 9% CP
6.5 kg of eventing cubes at say 11% CP $\Big\}$ = 10%

Check the hay/concentrate ratio: it is 48% to 52%.
Check the capacity: we are feeding 12.5 kg; the capacity is 15 kg.

STEP 6

Feed the ration, observe, consider and adjust if necessary.

Metrication

Land-based industries in Britain went metric in 1976 and ever since the feed room has been a muddle of metric and imperial. Now, with our close ties to mainland Europe, it is important that everyone in Britain tries to use metric measures.

Weight

If in doubt remember: 'Two and a quarter pounds of jam weigh about a kilogram.'

Pounds (lbs)	kilograms/pounds (kg/lbs)	kilograms (kg)
2.2	1	0.45
4.4	2	0.9
6.6	3	1.36
8.8	4	1.81
11.0	5	2.27
13.2	6	2.72
15.4	7	3.18
17.6	8	3.63
19.8	9	4.00

- Note the weight on sacks and containers.
- Resolve to make every feed board metric.

Appendix 2 – Metrication

Typically:

- Horse cubes come in 25 kg bags but some straight feeds come in 40 kg sacks. Fertiliser comes in 50 kg bags (used to be supplied in 1 cwt bags).
- Hay bales weigh about 25 kg (40 to the tonne).
- Straw bales weigh about 16.5 kg (60 to the tonne).
- Stacked hay takes up about 7 cubic metres per tonne.
- Stacked straw takes up 10.5 cubic metres per tonne.
- A hay crop of 10 tonnes per hectare used to be reckoned as 4 tons per acre. (A hectare is about 2.5 acres which is about the size of a professional football pitch.)
- A ton and a tonne (metric) are nearly the same.

Volume

- 1 litre is about 1¾ pints, or remember the phrase: 'A litre of water's a pint and three quarters.'
- We know from filling up with petrol at a garage that whereas we used to take 10 gallons we now take 45 litres.
- A 5 litre container holds just over 1 gallon.

APPENDIX 3
Useful Tables

TABLE 1 – Suggested ratio of hay to concentrates during fittening work		
Week 0	The horse is on maintenance alone	100% hay or grass
Week 1	Walking exercise 1 hour	Hay to concentrate 90%:10%
Week 2	Walking exercise about 1½ hours	Hay to concentrate 85%:15% to 80%:20%
Week 4	1½ hours walking and trotting	Hay to concentrate 80%:20% to 70%:30%
Week 6	1½ hours walking, trotting and cantering	Hay to concentrate 75%:25% to 60%:40%
Week 8	2 hours walking and cantering	Hay to concentrate 70%:30% to 50%:50%
Week 10	As before but including some fast work	Hay to concentrate 60%:40% to 40%:60%
Week 12	Starting competitions	Hay to concentrate 50%:50% to 35%:75%

Hay has been used in these tables as the 'roughage' ration. If other forages, such as vacuum-packed grass or lucerne, are used the protein level will need to be checked and the ratio altered to balance the ration.

TABLE 2 – Percentages of body weight as total dry food requirement						
Height in hands	*Girth in cms*	*Girth in inches*	*Body weight in kgs*	*Body weight in lbs*	*2%/3% in kgs*	*2%/3% in lbs*
12 hh	145 cms	57 ins	260 kgs	573 lbs	5.2–7.8	11–17
13 hh	155 cms	61 ins	320 kgs	705 lbs	6.4–9.6	14–21
14 hh	165 cms	64 ins	390 kgs	860 lbs	7.8–11.7	17–26
15 hh	180 cms	71 ins	490 kgs	1080 lbs	9.8–14.7	22–32
16 hh	195 cms	76 ins	580 kgs	1279 lbs	11.6–17.4	27–38
17 hh	205 cms	81 ins	640 kgs	1411 lbs	12.8–19.2	28–42
18 hh	215 cms	85 ins	710 kgs	1565 lbs	14.2–21.3	31–47

TABLE 3 – Nutritive value of some common foods		
	Crude Protein %	**Digestible Energy MJ/kg**
Cubes		
Horse and pony	10	10
Racehorse	13	13
Cereals		
Oats	12	14
Barley	11	15
Maize	9	17
Protein Foods		
Soya meal	49	16
Dried milk	36	17
Linseed	26	24
Field beans	26	16
Grass meal	12–18	13
Intermediate foods		
Wheat bran	16	12
Sugar beet pulp	9	14
Forage		
Good grass hay	9	11
Average grass hay	8	9
Poor grass hay	4	8
Grass silage	13–17	12
Haylage	16	11–12
Hydroponic barley 'grass'	16	17

Note: this table is only a guide and in practice a lot of variation will be found.

Bibliography

Ballière's Comprehensive Veterinary Dictionary, Ballière Tindall, 1988.

FRAPE, DAVID, *Equine Nutrition and Feeding*, Longman, 1986.

GOODY, PETER C., *Horse Anatomy*, J.A. Allen, 1983.

HOUGHTON-BROWN, JEREMY AND POWELL-SMITH, VINCENT, *Horse and Stable Management*, BSP Professional Books, 1984.

LAUNDER, E. AND LUCAS, D., *Feeding Facts*, D.J. Murphy, 1986.

PILLINER, SARAH, *Getting Horses Fit*, BSP Professional Books, 1986.

ROSSDALE AND WREFORD, *The Horse's Health from A to Z*, David and Charles, 1974.

Glossary

ADDITIVE	A substance added to food to improve palatability and/or keeping qualities, and to enhance appearance. When used to improve feed value it is known as a supplement.
ALIMENTARY CANAL	The route the food takes from mouth to anus and along which digestion and absorption take place.
ALLERGY	Sensitivity following second or subsequent exposure to some substances such as pollen, mould or dust that cause an adverse physical reaction.
AMINO ACIDS	The chief constituents of protein that are found naturally in plant and animal tissue. They consist of organic compounds containing the amino (NH_2) and the carboxyl (COOH) groups.
ANAEMIA	A deficiency of red blood cells and or haemoglobin.
ANEURYSM	A sac formed by the dilation of a wall of an artery, vein or the heart. An aneurysm is often the result of worm larvae damage which first produces a thrombosis on the inner wall.
ANTHELMINTIC	A drug or substance, normally given in food or by stomach tube or electuary, which kills worms.
ANUS	Opening at the end of the alimentary canal, through which faeces are expelled.
ASCORBIC ACID	Vitamin C.

Glossary

AZOTURIA   Also known as rhabdomyolysis (other names include 'tying-up', 'setfast' and 'Monday morning disease'). Stiffness and reluctance to move, painful stiff muscles over the back and quarters. Occurs after an unaccustomed exercise while on a heavy carbohydrate diet. Other causes still not fully understood.

BACTERIA   Single-cell micro-organisms that lack a true nucleus and organelles and multiply by dividing. Some are present in the gut and aid digestion. Other bacteria can cause disease.

BILE   An alkaline liquid that is secreted by the liver then poured into the small intestine when needed for digestion. It emulsifies, absorbs and digests fatty substances and neutralises acids.

BOLUS   A ball of food that has been chewed and is ready to be swallowed.

BOTULISM   Muscle paralysis which is due to damage of the muscle nerve supply. This damage is caused by a toxin produced by a bacterium called Clostridium botulinum, sometimes present in silage, to which horses are very susceptible.

Ca   The symbol for calcium.

CAECUM   Large comma-shaped sac which, together with the large and small colon, forms the hind gut, or large intestine. Bacterial fermentation of fibre takes place here.

CALCIUM (Ca)   Mineral needed for bone and tooth development, also for blood formation and clotting, muscle contraction, nervous system activity and lactation.

CALORIE   A unit of heat required to raise the temperature of 1 gram of water 1° Celsius. The amount of food capable of producing this amount of energy;

usually as the 'large calorie' equal to 1 kilocalorie (1000 cal).

CARBOHYDRATE A group of organic compounds containing carbon, hydrogen and oxygen. They include sugars, starches and cellulose.

CELLULOSE A structural carbohydrate which makes up a large part of plant matter. This passes into the hind gut where it is digested by micro-organisms.

CHALK Calcium carbonate. A soft fine-grained limestone, made up of tiny fossils.

CHLORINE (Cl) A chemical element which forms 'salts' with certain minerals, from which it can become dissociated in body fluids to become an electrolyte.

Cl Symbol for chlorine.

Co Symbol for cobalt.

COBALT A trace element. A component of vitamin B^{12}.

COMPOUND A substance made up of two or more materials. A foodstuff made up from several feed ingredients mixed together to provide an homogenous mixture.

COMPOUNDER A food merchant who makes up compound feeds.

COPD Chronic obstructive pulmonary disease.

COPPER (Cu) A trace element.

Cu The symbol for copper.

DEHYDRATION The state of the tissues and the blood when more fluid is lost from the body than is taken in. Water is more important to a horse's survival than food.

DIGESTA Food matter in the process of digestion.

DIGESTIBLE ENERGY The proportion of the potential energy in a feed which is in fact digested and absorbed.

DIURETIC Substance which alters the volume of body fluids by increasing the amount of urine passed.

Glossary

ELECTROLYTE   A chemical substance that when dissolved in water conducts electricity. The salts which dissociate into 'ions' are commercially called 'electrolytes' when used as supplements. Usually given to long-distance performance horses to offset loss by long sweating.

ELECTUARY   A powdered medicine, mixed into a paste with syrup, honey, molasses, etc. and smeared on the tongue.

ENTERITIS   Inflammation of the small intestine.

ENZYME   Any protein that acts as a catalyst and increases the rate at which a chemical reaction occurs. An animal body contains about 10,000 different enzymes.

EPIGLOTTIS   Small flap at the entrance to the larynx which, with other laryngeal cartilages, 'automatically' closes up at swallowing thus preventing food or water entering the trachea and so reaching the lungs.

EPIPHYSITIS   Inflammation of the epiphysis, the growth plate at the end of the long bones in young horses.

F   The symbol for fluorine.

FAECES   Waste matter passed from the bowels through the anus. Its consistency, colour and smell varies with diet and disease states.

Fe   The symbol for iron.

FIBRE   Dietary fibre consists of cellulose, hemicellulose, pectin and lignin which cannot be broken down by ordinary digestive juices. Crude fibre is a measurement in the composition of foodstuffs and is the residue after food has been treated with dilute acid and alkali. It is mainly cellulose and lignin.

FLUORINE (F)   Chemical element found in bones and teeth.

GASTRIC   Anything do to with the stomach.

GLAND   Small organ which produces fluids from the blood: e.g. sweat, saliva, mucus, milk.

130

GLUCOSE	A carbohydrate; a 'simple' or monosaccharide form of sugar. It is the major source of energy for living organisms.
GLYCOGEN	A stored form of carbohydrate; a polysaccharide also called animal starch.
GRAIN	Seed of cereal plant.
GUT	Another name for intestine, bowel or alimentary canal.
HAEMOGLOBIN	A protein and iron constituent of red blood cells. It transports oxygen, taking it up from the lungs and releasing it to the tissues. Oxygenated haemoglobin, as in arteries, is bright red.
I	The symbol for iodine.
ILEUM	End of the small intestine which opens into the caecum.
INCISORS	Front biting teeth.
INTESTINAL FLORA	The bacteria and protozoa in the large intestine.
IODINE (I)	A chemical element essential to the function of the thyroid gland.
IRON (Fe)	An important chemical element, an essential part of the red pigment in red blood cells.
JEJUNUM	Part of the small intestine.
JOULE	A unit of energy. Energy is expressed as the number of joules in a kilogram of food.
K	The symbol for potassium.
KIDNEY	Organ which removes waste products and water from the blood, forming urine.
LAMINITIS	Inflammation of the sensitive laminae (the membrane that lines the pedal bone and interlocks with the insensitive laminae). This causes heat and pain, resulting in severe lameness.

Glossary

LAXATIVE — An additive which eases the passage of material through the gut.

LIGNIN — Woody, indigestible portion of dietary roughage.

LYSINE — An important naturally occurring amino acid.

MACRO-MINERAL — Minerals needed in relatively large amounts in the diet as opposed to trace minerals. They include calcium, phosphorus, magnesium, potassium, sodium and sulphur.

MAGNESIUM (Mg) — A mineral, important for the correct functioning of muscle, bone, teeth and enzyme systems.

MAINTENANCE DIET — A diet that is sufficient to maintain in a state of health a horse that is not working.

MALNUTRITION — Bad nutrition caused by a lack of food, the wrong type of food or the inefficient absorption of food.

MANGANESE (Mn) — Metallic trace element.

MEGA — Unit of measurement: 1 million times basic unit.

MEGAJOULE — Because there are so many joules in a kilogram, they are expressed as megajoules or MJ. They are used to describe the Digestible Energy, or DE, of a particular type of food.

METABOLISM — Continuous chemical processes taking place in the body which are essential for life to be sustained.

METHIONINE — An essential amino acid.

Mg — The symbol for magnesium.

MICRO — Very small.

MICRO-MINERALS — Also called trace elements; required by the horse in minute quantities. They include copper, iron, iodine, zinc, manganese, selenium and cobalt.

MICRO-ORGANISMS — Very small organisms that can be seen only through a microscope, usually bacteria and fungi. Viruses are ultra-microscopic, i.e.

cannot be seen through an ordinary 'light' microscope.

MINERALS Inorganic substances which are neither animal nor vegetable. In small amounts they are an essential part of the diet.

Mn The symbol for manganese.

MOLARS Large 'back' teeth adapted for grinding food.

Na The symbol for sodium.

NICOTINIC ACID Also known as niacin. White crystals or powder classed as a B vitamin; it is essential for normal carbohydrate metabolism.

NUTS Compounded feed mixtures, compressed into small cylindrical pieces, suitable for feeding to horses.

OESOPHAGUS The gullet: a muscular tube which extends from the pharynx to the stomach.

ORGANIC Substances of either animal or vegetable composition. They all contain carbon, hydrogen and oxygen in fixed ratios. Proteins also contain nitrogen.

P The symbol for phosphorus.

PANCREAS A gland in the abdomen. It secretes a substance into the duodenum which helps to digest the food. A second substance – the hormone insulin – is secreted directly into the bloodstream and is essential for the control of glucose levels in the blood.

PARASITE An organism living in or on another. The parasite nourishes itself to varying degrees at the expense of the host and/or obtains 'shelter'.

PARROT MOUTH A short lower jaw, resulting in the incorrect meeting of top and bottom teeth, producing overgrowth of the upper incisors and first and last molars. The incisor 'bite' may be lost, depending on degree of undershooting.

Glossary

PERISTALSIS   The rhythmic muscular contractions of the alimentary canal which propel the gut contents towards the rectum.

pH   The symbol used to express acidity or alkalinity. pH 7 is neutral. Above pH 7, the alkalinity is higher; and below it, acidity increases.

PHARYNX   The throat.

PHOSPHORUS (P)   An essential mineral; needed for bone development and in most of the metabolic processes.

POTASSIUM (K)   A mineral essential for bodily health, especially for maintenance of acid-base and water balance notably in red blood cells and muscles.

PROTEIN   A complex organic compound composed of chains of amino acids; it is an essential ingredient of all living matter.

QUIDDING   Dropping out of partially chewed food from the mouth. It is usually due to pain associated with teeth problems but can also be caused by other inflammations in the mouth and from inability to swallow.

RECTUM   The last portion of the intestine between the small colon and the anus.

RHABDOMYOLYSIS   See AZOTURIA.

SALINE   A solution of salt.

SALIVA   A colourless fluid containing a digestive enzyme produced by glands in the mouth.

Se   The symbol for selenium.

SELENIUM (Se)   A trace element.

SET-FAST   See AZOTURIA.

SODIUM (Na)   A mineral essential for bodily health.

SODIUM CHLORIDE   Common salt. A necessary constituent of the body.

STOMACH	Part of the alimentary tract between the oesophagus and the small intestine.
THIAMIN	Vitamin B_1.
TRACHEA	The windpipe, through which air passes to the lungs.
TRYPTOPHAN	An important amino acid.
VITAMIN	One of a number of organic chemical substances which are present in various foods and essential to health.
ZINC (Zn)	A trace element.
Zn	The symbol for zinc.

Index

A

Age 74–5, 80
Ailments 99–102
Alfalfa 55
  pellets 90
Alveoli 105
Amino-acids 43, 53
Anaemia 47, 50, 97
Anorexia 48
Antacids 30
Antibiotics 68
Appetite, poor 47
Apples 63
Availability of foodstuffs 76
Azoturia 58, 101–2

B

Bad doers 96–7
Barley 59, 108
  grass 41, 63
  mash 108
  straw 56
Bars of mouth 29
Beans 62, 65
Beech 63
Beta-carotene 48
Bins, storage 111
Biotin 50

Blood 11, 20, 41, 97
Body 11
Bones 48
Botulism 55
Box (shrub) 63
Box walking 99
Bran 40, 46, 60
  as 'opener' 33
  mash 90, 107–9
Breadmeal 60
Brewers' grains/yeast 62
Broodmares 48, 65
  see also Mares
Buckets 16, 112
Bulk food 41, 43, 51–7, 61
  see also Roughage

C

Cabbage leaves 63
Caecum 28, 32, 41
Calciferol 48
Calcium 45–6, 48, 64, 66, 94
Cancer 97
Carbohydrates 28, 42–3, 59, 66, 75, 94
Carotene 40, 48, 63
Carrots 40, 48, 63
Cell membranes 44

Index

Cellulose 28, 32, 42
Cereals 45–6, 57–61, 76, 92
  see also Barley, Oats, Maize, Wheat
Chaff 39, 56–7, 107
Chlorine 46
Chlorophyll 27
Chocolate 63, 83
Choking 34
Chop 56–7
Circuit breaker 113
Cleanliness 110
Clover 54–5
Coarse mixes 62, 65
Cobalt 47
Cocoa 63, 83
Cod liver oil 48
Colic 39, 53, 63, 97, 100–1
Colon 32, 35
Colonic impaction 101
Comfrey 64
Competition horses
  feeding 65–6
  watering 17–18
Compound mixtures 57, 64–6, 91
Concentrates 33, 57–68, 78, 80
  for event horses 84–5
  for hunters 84–5
  for ponies 92
  preparation of 106–7
  storage of 110–12
Condition 38, 70–3
COPD 39, 102, 105
Copper 47
Corn 33
  oil 86
  syrup 86
Cornea, inflammation of 48

Cost effectiveness 76
Cottonseed 61
Coughing 105
Cubes 62, 65, 90, 94, 102
  lucerne 56

D
Dandelions 40, 64, 98
Defaecation 34
Dehydration 12, 18–22, 101
Dental care 36
Diarrhoea 22, 101
Digestion 11, 25–37, 41
Digestive system 30–31
Digestive tract 28
Doping rules 84
Dressage horses 87–8
Droppings 11, 34–5
Dust 102, 105

E
Economy 76, 81, 90–1
Electrolytes 17–18, 21–22, 30, 35, 86, 99
  imbalance of 101
Energy 25, 78
  sources of 28, 33, 44
Enzyme action 47
Epiphysitis 79, 93, 100, 102
Equipment 110–14
Event horses 17, 43–4, 71, 84–5
  rations for 84–5
Excretory areas 34
Exercise 34
Eyes 12

F
Faeces 11, 34–5
Fat 71–3

Fats 44, 97
Fatty acids 28
Feeding 26, 41, 96–102
  equipment 110–14
  problems of 96–102
  rules and times of 38–41
  see also Concentrates, Food,
    Foodstuffs, Ration,
    Roughage
Fibre 42–3, 59
  see also Roughage
Fish meal 57, 62
Fittening 123
Foals 93–4, 106
  feeding 48, 62, 65
  diarrhoea 22, 101
  protein for 43, 61, 79
  watering 15
Folic acid 50–66
Food 25–37, 41
  changes in 39–40
  preparing 103–9
  refusal of 96–9
  storage of 110–14
  types of 51–68
  see also Concentrates,
    Feeding, Foodstuffs,
    Roughage
Foodstuffs 39, 76–7
  nutritional value 77–8
  types of 51–68
  see also Concentrates,
    Feeding, Food, Roughage
Fungal spores 102, 104, 112

G
Garlic 64, 102
Geldings 101
Glucose 22, 58

Glycogen 58
Grains 33, 58
Grass 28–9, 32, 40, 43, 98
  as hay 54
  cubes 107
  dried 56
  molassed 107
  vacuum-packed 55–6
  vitamins in 48
Grazing 33–4, 40, 46, 76, 90
Grooming, mutual 34
Growth, poor 48
Gullet 32
Gut bacteria 49, 58, 107–8
  see also Micro-organisms in
    digestive tract

H
Haemoglobin 47
Hay 33, 48, 82, 102
  alfalfa 55
  as roughage 32, 39, 43, 52–3,
    80
  clover 55
  feeding methods 103–6
  for event horses 84–5
  for riding school horses 90
  for youngstock 94
  lucerne 55
  meadow 54–5
  mowburnt 52
  nets 103, 106
  new/old 40, 53
  seed 54
  soaking 104–5
  storage of 76, 111–12
  types of 53–55
Haylage 55–7
Herbs 64

Hoof formation 102
Hormone abnormalities 102
Hunters 18, 89–90
Hydrocyanic acid 109
Hydroponically grown 'grass' 41, 63

I
Incisors 29
Infertility 48
Intestines 28, 32, 41
Iodine 64
Iron 64

J
Joints 12, 48

L
Laburnum 63
Lactic acid 58
Lameness 100, 102
Laminitis 53, 58, 63, 82, 92, 102
Lawn mowings 63
Laxative 98
Legs, filled 53, 58
Legumes 57, 62
Lime (tree) 63
Linase enzyme 109
Linseed 57, 60–1
   mash 108–9
Lips 29
Liver 47, 97
Long-distance riding horses 18, 44, 85
Lucerne 55, 57, 98
   cubes 56, 86, 107
   molassed 107
Lymph 11
Lymphangitis 102

Lysine 43, 66

M
Magnesium 46
Maintenance ration 70, 74, 78, 80, 98
   for stallions 95
   seasonal 82–3
Maize 46, 60
Mares
   azoturia in 101
   brood 48, 65
   lactating 12, 43, 79, 93
   pregnant 74, 78, 93
   watering 15
Mashes 107–8
Mastication 29–33
Megajoules 78
Metabolism 38, 44, 74, 97, 102
Methionine 43, 66
Metrication 121–2
Micro-organisms
   contamination by 41
   in digestive tract 28, 32, 43, 49, 58, 68
Milk 12
   powder 57, 62
Minerals 40, 44–7, 62, 65–6, 98
   deficiency in 102
Mints 63
Molars 29
Molasses 46, 57, 63–5, 98, 107
Monday morning disease 58, 101–2
Mould spores 102, 104, 112
Mouth 30
Muscle 71–3

N
Nettles 64
Night blindness 48
Nostrils 12
Nutritional values 125

O
Oat straw 56, 83
Oatmeal gruel 109
Oats 59, 82, 108
Oils 44
    cod liver 48
    corn 86
    wheatgerm 49
Older horses 75
One-horse owner 40, 52, 81, 91,
    105, 107
'Openers' 33–4, 61, 106–7

P
Pallets 112
Pans, feed 112–13
    see also Equipment
Parasitism 76
Pea pods 63
Peas 62, 65
Phosphorus 45–6, 48, 66
'Pinch' test 20
Plants
    characteristics of 27–8
    garden 63
Point-to-pointers 88–9
Poisonous shrubs 63
Polo ponies 89
Polydypsia 22
Polyuria 22
Ponies 7–8, 83, 91–3
Potassium 46
Power point 113

Probiotics 68
Prohibited substances 83–4, 88
Prostaglandins 44
Protein 43, 59, 62, 75, 78, 83
    for competition horses 83–4
    for youngstock 94

R
Racehorses 83
Ragwort 53, 97
Ration 117–20, 123–4
    deciding on a 69–81
    for different types of horse
        82–95
    maintenance 70, 74, 78, 80,
        95, 98
Respiratory disorders 48
Rest, enforced 98
Retinol 48
Rhabdomyolysis 46, 58, 101–2
Riding school horses 90–1
Rock salt 67
Rose prunings 63
Roughage 39, 51–7, 66, 80,
    84–5, 90, 92
    see also Chaff, Fibre, Grass,
    Hay, Haylage, Silage, Straw
Routine 33–4

S
Saliva 30, 32
Salivation 34
Salt 45, 66–7, 86, 107, 111
Scales 113
Seaweed 64
Selenium 44, 46–7, 49, 66, 86
Set fast 46, 58, 101–2
Show jumpers 89
Shrubs, poisonous 63

Sick horse 97–8
Silage 55
Size 73–4, 80
Skin 11
Smell, sense of 41
Sodium 46
  see also Salt
Soya bean meal 46, 62, 65
Stallions 94–5, 101
Starch 28, 42, 59
Stomach 32, 35, 39, 41
Storage of foodstuffs 110–14
Straw 43, 86
  barley 56
  oat 83, 90
Stress 96, 98–9, 101
Succulents 40–1, 48
Sugar 42, 109
  cubes 63
Sugar beet 46, 57, 82–3, 90, 94
  as 'opener' 33, 39, 61, 88, 107
  COPD 102
  for sick horses 95
  soaking 106
Sunflower seed 61
Sunlight 48, 111
Supplements 66–8, 84–6, 94, 105
Sweating 21–2
Sweet itch 64
Sycamore 63

T
Teeth 29, 36–7, 100
Temperament 38, 75, 80
Tendons, contracted 79, 93, 100, 102
Thiamine 50
Thirst, excessive 22

Thoroughbreds 90, 94
Throat 30
'Thumps' 20
Titbits 63
Tocopherol 49
Tongue 29
Toxicity problems 84
Trace elements 44–7, 62, 64
Travelling 89, 102
  dehydration during 21–2, 40
Trickle feeders 12, 28–9, 39
Tryptophan 43
Turf 64
Tushes 29
Tying up 46, 58, 101–2
Types of horses 73–4, 80

U
Urination, excessive 22
Urine 11

V
Vacuum-packed grass 55–6, 102, 111
Ventilation 102
Vermin 41, 55, 111–12
Veterinary surgeon 96–7, 101, 105
Vitamins 40, 47–50, 65–66, 78, 98, 102
  vitamin A 48, 66
  vitamin B12 62, 64, 66
  vitamin D 48, 66
  vitamin E 44, 49, 60, 66, 86
  vitamin K 49
  water soluble 49–50
Vomiting 32

W
Water 11–14, 20–1, 35, 41, 113
Watering 17–18
  principles of 12–14
  systems for stabled horses
   15–16
Weaning 93
Weather 75–6
Weaving 99
Weight 71–3, 124
Wheat 60
Wheatgerm oil 49, 60

Wild horses 7, 45
Work 38, 79–81
Worms 22, 36, 96–7, 101

Y
Young horses 22, 106
  protein for 43, 61, 75, 79
  supplements for 45, 48
  rations for 74, 94

Z
Zebras 7